JACK THE LAD RN

The collected drivel, doodles and ditties of a dedicated dabtoe

JACK THE LAD RN

The collected drivel, doodles and ditties of a dedicated dabtoe

TED MACEY

Alias –
Ted of the Med, Clubs of the Cossack, That bloody clubswinger, That
waterlogged old Bath-steward, Lt (SD) (PT) EJ Macey, ACP,
Cert Ed (failed ~~bed~~ B Ed) RN (Rtd)

AND

MERRY SWAN

Matador
5 Weir Road
Kibworth Beauchamp
Leicester LE8 0LQ, UK
Tel: (+44) 116 279 2299
Fax: 0116 279 2277
Email: books@troubador.co.uk
Web: www.troubador.co.uk/matador

ISBN 978 1848761 896

British Library Cataloguing in Publication Data.
A catalogue record for this book is available from the British Library.

Typeset in 11pt Book Antiqua by Troubador Publishing Ltd, Leicester, UK
Printed in the UK by TJ International, Padstow, Cornwall

Matador is an imprint of Troubador Publishing Ltd

Ted's Dedication

to

My children Nicholas, Ian, Simon and Meredeth who ... 'thought their Dad was quite a clown'

and to

all the fellow Clubswingers, Shipmates and Officers who tolerated me for 24 years

A Dedication on my Dad's behalf

To Laura, Lucy, Tiffany, Ross, Marina and Elizabeth – the third generation

Ted's Acknowledgements

To all those I may have rubbed up the wrong way at various times during my Service Career, who think they may recognise themselves, the incident or event in these collected works.

To the readers of: -

The Pompey Magazine	RNB, Portsmouth.
The Communicator	HMS Mercury, Petersfield
The Shotley Magazine	HMS Ganges, Ipswich
The Clubswinger	Temeraire, Portsmouth
Contact	Culverhouse School Magazine, South Ockendon, Essex

… who may have seen much of this material before… sorreeey… I'm imposing it on you again.

To Mrs Josie Holly, who laboured over a hot typewriter, so that even I could read (most of) what I had written, and who has made it presentable for you to read.

Disclaimer

If you think you recognise yourself... forget it. It must have been two other blokes.

Spelling mistakes, bad grammar, and misprints may be blamed on my ownership of a notoriously illiterate and bad-spelling typewriter. Do NOT (R) NOT shoot the typesetter, he had enough trouble trying to decipher it anyway.

Further Acknowledgements

As my father's daughter – I wish to reiterate all of the above – and also add for those of you (and families related) who recognise yourselves or yours; please accept my profound thanks. I believe my father never had anything derogatory or malice towards anyone he mentioned. I also believe that he held those mentioned in high regard and with great respect.

One specific person I wish to acknowledge is someone whose information has made a significant impact on this book – Rick Jolly OBE – with his many years of research into naval terms and expressions, and outstanding author of '*Jackspeak*'. He has gracefully allowed me to use his research in order to understand and translate my Dad's stories more clearly.

A Special Word about HMS Cossack (LO3, FO3, GO3)

While I was compiling this book, I was also researching and checking dates and timelines. It was only after my father's death in 1982 that I discovered a cap tally of HMS Cossack buried in his belongings. I realised three of the stories referred to a time he had spent on this ship. I began to discover the modesty of a true naval man. My Dad must have been very proud to be associated with a ship of such high distinction, yet was probably just pleased to survive the ardour of war and live life another day.

As a result of more exploration I found www.hmscossack.org, leading me to a welcoming and friendly group of people by way of the HMS Cossack Association. The stories written in my father's own words may be found in HMS Cossack Association's archives. I am compelled to mention the association's warm and special 'ship's company' - a great credit to the HMS Cossacks and the Royal Navy. So this is in remembrance of her, her crews and their durability, expressing the courage and endurance of ALL men associated with her name.

Battle Honours

Baltic 1835
Dover Patrol 1914 -1919
Narvik 1940
Norway 1940
Atlantic 1940 – 1941
Bismarck Action 1941
Malta Convoys 1941

Pennant numbers LO3, FO3, GO3 from 1938 – 1941; credited with "The Altmark Incident", "The Navy's Here", "Vian of the Cossack", "The Daily Mirror Ship" and her sister ship HMS Afridi.

Contents

Ted's Timeline

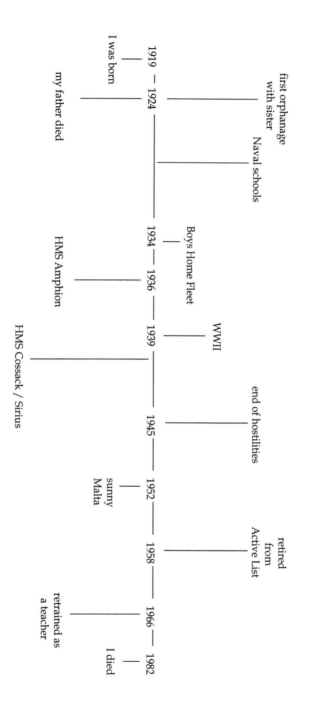

first orphanage
with sister

Naval schools

I was born

1919 — 1924

my father died

Boys Home Fleet

1934 — 1936

HMS Amphion

WWII

1939

HMS Cossack / Sirius

end of hostilities

1945

sunny
Malta

1952

retired
from
Active List

1958

retrained as
a teacher

1966 — 1982

I died

Ted's Family Tree

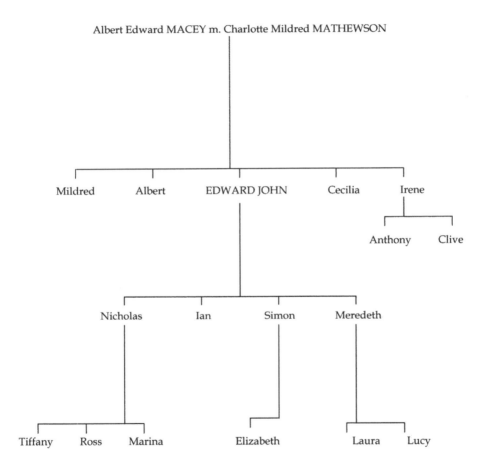

Albert Edward MACEY m. Charlotte Mildred MATHEWSON

Mildred   Albert   EDWARD JOHN   Cecilia   Irene

Anthony   Clive

Nicholas   Ian   Simon   Meredeth

Tiffany   Ross   Marina   Elizabeth   Laura   Lucy

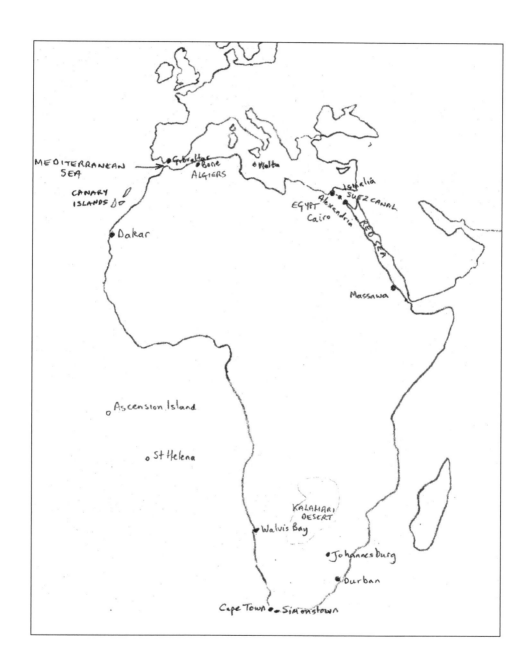

Ted's Africa Map

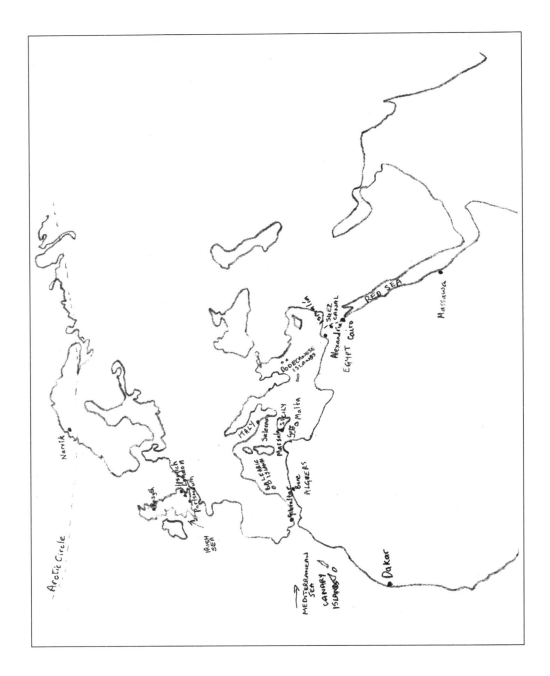

Ted's Mediterranean Map

Foreword

As the youngest of Ted's four children, I grew up in a post-Royal Navy era of family life and only knew his civilian world as a teacher. My father told me he was 'writing a book' - it was based on his younger life. His 'young life' however, turns out to have been much enriched. Lt Ted Macey RN was a man of sincerity, passion and humour. The Royal Navy was his life. Starting off at five years old in a naval orphanage he worked his way through WW2 and the RN ranks, with hopes and dreams of a better future for all of his kin.

Jack the Lad RN is a matelot's wit set in verse, odes and prose, with over 140 cartoons. This is an open illustration of the true spirit in the Royal Navy and beyond, never waning through ranks or years. In my father's works you will discover humour and humility behind the history; making the best of a childhood despite being put in an orphanage, seeing the lighter side of life during WW2 despite being torpedoed and bombed, enjoying the dizzy heights of naval Physical Training Officer despite the looming prospect of being taken off the Active List and finally settling down to some schoolwork again despite being a teacher – an ordinary man with an ordinary life?

After Dad's death a memento I lay claim to was 'the manuscript', so it was agreed amongst my siblings. The 13 short stories are based on events my father experienced - his encounters he had written down or passed on by word-of-mouth. I acquired Ted's service records in order to substantiate many of the real events. I now see a fragment of what he may have been going through when he sacrificed so much for us.

So here is an ordinary Royal Navy man's light-hearted lifetime collection of reminiscences; set in poetry, prose and cartoons.

– 1919 to 1982 –

Here's to you Dad

This dolly daughter has produced for you, along with siblings,
Off springs who, in turn will come to know the love you gave in life.
Be of good cheer – although you're missed, your life lives on through
us.

Let's hope your works, for all to see, inspire and 'educate'
Others who may come to read these doodlings and jottings fine,
And begin to see another time and generation past, through your eyes
of passion.

Fondest love always
Nil Desperandum

Introduction

(by Admiral Sir James Eberle, GCB, LLD, RN)

This book tells a story. More accurately it tells a few stories, combined with cartoons, verse (sometimes doggerel) and 'odd odes', which together provide a uniquely drawn picture of life in the Royal Navy. This has been moulded in the stress of service during WWII and thereafter, as a new generation of young people under the guidance of their wartime leaders, struggled to rebuild a world which had been deeply damaged both materially and morally.

This book was originally written by a young man Ted Macey, who joined the Royal Navy as a Boy Seaman in 1934 and retired as a Naval Officer in 1958. It has been put together by his daughter, following his death in 1982. Like the content of a good meal, this thoroughly entertaining book deserves to be best tasted in small pieces.

Ted shows himself to be an acute observer of people and events. His service in the Navy was as a member of the Physical Training branch (a PTI or a *club swinger*' in naval parlance). The centre of his naval service was therefore sport, which in one way or other touched the lives of everyone on board every ship of the Royal Navy. He was thus in a unique position to be an acute observer of ship borne life – and was able to represent its inevitable 'ups and downs' – to observe the individual reaction of all members of the ship's company and to chronicle the language and attitudes of both the 'lower deck' sailors and the wardroom officers.

This book is fun – fun which has always played a strong part in my own life. In 1979 when I was privileged to be appointed as Commander in Chief of the British Fleet, the first signal to all ships of the fleet that I made was *"I wish my officers and men of the Fleet to know that I regard fun as an essential ingredient of efficiency and not as a detriment to it"*. I also shared Ted's fascination with horses – and departed all my senior naval appointments mounted on a horse.

Ted and I both served in *HMS Cossack*, a ship's name which remains cherished in naval history for its gallant rescue from the *Altmark* of British seamen captured by the Germans from British shipping sunk in the Atlantic in 1940. I am therefore honoured to strongly recommend this book, from which a donation has been pledged to the 'Help for Heroes' charity. It provides a unique experience, especially for bedside reading, to all who have connections with the sea and the Royal Navy – and to the many that have not yet had this privilege.

"Admiral Jim"

Don't scrump – you'll get a thump
or
Mind my Bike

The gate was high – beyond – a feast –
in a tall wall – seven foot – at least.
Since I am seven – and only small –
how can I climb – a seven-foot wall?

A motorbike against the wall –
stand on the seat – make me quite tall.
Fingertips hook – that's quite nice –
what does that spell ... P...O...L... ice?

I can't spell – don't know that word –
bike shouldn't be here – it's quite absurd.
Pull and kick – and strain quite hard –
to get into – that farmers yard.

That kick produced an awful clatter –
I wonder then – what is the matter?
The other side now – I'm in clover –
do you think that motorbike – fell over?

Pick up the fallers – and stuff in pocket –
if farmer comes – I'll run like rocket.
Wish I could climb tree – and get some more –
who's that standing – at farmhouse door?

Barking farm dog – a deathly pallor –
discretion the better part of valour.
Drop off wall – arms of law – beneath –
at least they haven't got – long sharp teeth.

"Now what's this 'ere then – who've I caught?"
"All those apples – you ain't bought".
"Scrumping apples – that act's criminal –
kick my bike over – that's almost terminal".

"These 'ere apples – I'll have to take –
to show my Sergeant – why I'm back late.
Buzz off now – or I'll clip your ear –
if I find you again – round here".

Munching apples then – makes radio report –
whilst seven year old – holds back retort.
Then sidles off – and near Tillage clock –
pulls two more apples – from his sock.

Well worthwhile – this little spree –
and dawdles homeward – for his tea.
"Your Auntie's been – why do you hide?"
"She left you a bowl full of apples – on the side".

Dreams and the dreamer (1)

The Happiest Days

Jarring, jangling, ringing sound –
leap from bed in one swift bound.
Bathroom ablutions – splash about –
bangs and clatters – and loud shout.

The schoolboy starts his hectic day –
usually in this sort of way.
Quickly dress and down the stair –
rumpled shirt, jacket – half dried hair.

Kitchen for short breakfast halt –
before he does his usual bolt.
Cornflakes, toast and marmalade –
more than that – Mum can't persuade.

At door – asks for football boots –
passing mate gives derisive hoots.
Chases mate along the road –
bag, boots and books – quite a load.

Swinging bag makes weapon fair –
catches mate – and parts his hair.
Then they wrestle for a while –
arrive at school – not quite in style.

Playground then to kick around –
a ball, but tin can makes more sound.
Bell then rings – and Master's shouting –
drag feet inside – grimace and pouting.

Energy has died – stone dead –
wishes he were back in bed.
Register first – then Assembly Hall –
trip up mate – and make him fall.

Accused by Master – looks surprised –
can't hide laughter from his eyes.
"Not me Sir – would I ever?" –
hopes that Master's not too clever.

Sit and squirm – Headmaster spouting –
tells boy in front – he'll get a clouting.
Sitting next to Susie Spry –
"Break-time, I will black your eye".

Kick her ankles under chair –
then he tries to pull her hair.
Cause disturbance in the ranks –
up to usual schoolboy pranks.

Into classroom – maths to start –
not done homework – in the cart.
Struggle through a sum or two –
hopes to dodge – "Please Sir – the loo?".

Master's heard it all before –
"Not a chance – do question four".
Sit a while – and try to think –
"Please Sir, my pen's run out of ink".

Release is shortly to be found –
break time bell – a joyful sound.
Rush outside – all smiles again –
crisps from tuck shop – try them plain.

Kick tin can again – and shout –
abuse – at lanky playground lout.
Get chased for cheek – dodge and turn –
to hold his tongue – he'll never learn.

Into school again with bell –
rush down corridor – pell-mell.
First in classroom – slam the door –
keep them out – done this before.

Master arrives then – just his luck –
"Please Sir, the blinking door was stuck".
"I know young Smith, you think me a bore –
I've heard these yarns from you before".

"If I cane you now – you'll think me savage –
why not try being – the normal – average?"
"In your desk – and sit down quick –
before I look around – for stick".

English lesson can then proceed –
Smithy here – takes little heed.
Till called upon – to stand on feet –
"What did I say – will you please repeat?"

Lunchtime comes – so – off with chums –
playing cowboys – shooting guns.
Chips – at local fish shop then –
still playing – gangsters, guns, G-men.

Return to school – for next session –
History then – a tiring lesson.
What did he say, he had six wives? –
my cat, Tinker – has got nine lives...

Football after break – that's good –
their goalie stands like block of wood.
Receive the ball – run like mad –
slide it past him – he does look sad.

In to change – then – late back home –
"Up and bath – while I'm on the phone".
"Not yet Mum – not today" –
"It's still quite light – I've got time to play".

Hay Burners Ahoy (I)

by Merry Swan

Ted's tender years led his dreams of life with horses far away from his preceding encounters with the milkman's horse at the age of four. That was, until 1934 and his selection for the Boys Team of the Home Fleet, in the Royal Tournament at Olympia. He was going to be part of a rope climbing and window ladder display party for the Royal Navy, and once there, have close contact to hay burners in the form of P Battery Royal Horse Artillery.

Bert and Ted had just finished their first rehearsal in the big arena and had to clear out quickly as the RHA were due on. "Let's stay and watch the RHA, Bert. We might get a go on a horse when we all do the mock Tournament at the end of this tour", Ted urged. So Bert and Ted took ringside positions and sat mesmerised by the skill and speed of the moves by the riders and their four-legged partners towing the gun carriages and limbers.

Afterwards Ted and Bert decided to follow the horsemen down to the stables. "Hey Ted, look at those brown jobs and their hay burners. They've got two in each stall, haven't they?" Bert blurted out. "...You know, I used to dream of owning a horse, and being able to fly over hedges and gates in the countryside." Ted's voice began to drift away from Bert, as he gazed longingly into one of the stables. He was brought back to reality with a bump as a stableman swung a bridle on to the stable door right in front of Ted's face. "Blimey, that's pretty shiny. I can see my reflection in the leather bits too!" Ted gasped. Bob the stableman looked up, "Hey mate, sorry about that. I'm glad somebody's noticed my hard work" Bob said, as he retrieved the bridle from the door. "This harness takes hours of polishing to get it like that – it's quite knackering actually. Perhaps you fancy coming down here another day and giving it a go".

Bob had a strange half smile on his face as he spoke. Ted hadn't noticed though. He was too busy trying to lean over and stroke one of the horses now. Bert laughed at the stableman and said, "Not on your Nelly. We only came down here to look, not to work!"

However, Ted found his way back to the stables a few more times after that. He struck up a close friendship with Bob but found that Bob never seemed to have any time away from the horses, so Ted spent all of his spare time down in the stables amongst the hay burners. This was a far cry from the rigid and regimented ways of his temporary barracks. There was only a certain amount of time the boys could practise their moves on the ropes in the arena, as other groups needed their own practise time for a variety of spectacles. With a bit of bargaining from the start, Ted and one or two other naval boys found themselves buffing harness, shackles, drags and so on in the warmth of the stables. Under Bob's watchful eye Ted brushed, polished and combed one of the horses too. There was a special relationship shining out between horse and groom. "I get on really well with Magic. Let me take him out tomorrow morning", Ted begged of Bob. "It'll cost you. If I get caught I'd be put on a charge and no questions asked", Bob began, but Ted had the ideal answer. Bob was bound to agree, especially as the exercising always took place so very early in the mornings, well before any senior officers would be about.

Those pre-war days saw the Services food rations vary across the board, with the Navy faring better than the Army, and naval boys in training had a special ration above the victual allowance of a naval rating. Needless to say, this food had almost as much bargaining power as a tot. Consequently a certain amount of surplus Navy food found its way to the stables at Olympia with some Army drivers, Bob included, managing to put weight on during the Tournament period.

So picture this – Army horses being exercised up Kensington High Street, into Hyde Park and along Rotten Row each morning between about 05:30 and 06:00 but with the occasional mounted sailor suit. Perhaps not Ted's ideal of countryside with hedges, but he had never ridden a proper horse before so this was quite an experience for the young lad; especially as these exercises took place without saddles for the riders, so comfort and control was almost impossible for Ted. However the horses all seemed to know where they were going and obligingly followed one another.

The Tournament culmination for all the men would be the mock set-up on the Saturday morning following three hard weeks of polished public performances. They all had a chance to swap talents and have a go at some of each other's skills. For a few charitable copper donations in buckets, the public were treated to the finest show of disorganised chaos likely to be seen anywhere.

It was the Royal Navy's turn. "Come on lads, we can do it!" shouted Ted to his contemporaries. A line of horses walked neatly out from the stable exit, and then began their trot. For about five minutes mayhem ensued as some 50 budding Lester Piggots in sailors' uniforms tried to sort out port from starboard, rules of the road and who had right of way, as the horses continued to do their own thing with a quiet nip on the rump or a sly hoof at a stable-mate. Before any real damage was caused to the horses, the Army played their trump card and opened the stable doors. This had the same effect on the horses as Up Spirits had on a dabtoe working. The hay burners galloped hightail for their stalls, all converging in a heap at the door and wearing sailors round their necks and bellies. Ted faired no better than anyone else.

"The best 'Blinker' class I've had this term…"

However, Ted and the others did manage a laugh when they then saw their senior officers, with saddles, one by one attempting various jumps with some success, until the Army Captain of the Horse played his trump card with a sharp crack of the whip. At this, most of the horses stopped dead in their tracks, just at take-off pace, allowing the rider to complete the jump on his own with a front somersault and a brake fall in six.

There were many bruises being nursed by the next day, but many smiles to soothe the sores too and one or two Staff Officers walking round with limps and sour grapes for the Army.

Ode to the Flu

Je ne sais pas – what to do
Now I've caught this bout of flu.
Whisky, lemon – blankets piled high,
crawl into bed – hope I don't die.

Naval Terms Illustrated – "Gripes"

Ode to Summer Holidays

Soft falls the gentle rain –
In Southern France and sunny Spain.
Money, passport – blonde barmaid too –
I bet, on your hols – it'll rain on you.

"Hey Tubby – you took HET maths –
how many pints of plonk to a litre."

Ode to the Yacht Club

To a salt water sailor on a concrete sea –
The waves aren't as big as they used to be.
Nostalgia gets him by the throat –
Fiddling now in a glass fibre boat.

Delivery Service

Postman plodding – in pouring rain –
Soaked right through – feet in pain.
Parcel to deliver – no answer yet –
Leave on doorstep – to get soaking wet.

Sandscratcher Supreme

by Merry Swan

The ex-director of PT and sports was casting his net around Pompey to commission a cruiser as the flagship of 6th Cruiser Squadron for the South Africa Station. The captain had a two and a half-year stretch left before retirement from the Active List. His intended final fling in the Royal Navy was to take his brand new flag ship and his brand new Ship's Company and win every sports trophy on that station.

As a Boy in the Royal Navy, Ted had just completed six months training for a pre-war Royal Tournament at Olympia and subsequently found himself 'volunteered' (from here to the left) as part of the Boys Division for the new Ship's Company.

Following two and half months showing their presence in the Canary Islands and the Boys continuing their training in preparation for the Empire Exhibition, they finally set course for Africa. They were to be involved in Johannesburg's Navy Week as part of the Empire Exhibition and the city's Golden Jubilee.

"Hey Ted. Have you heard? We're going down the Robertson Mine!" Charlie was running into the Mess as he was shouting. Several other Boys, all previously busy, appeared from behind bulkheads and lockers, hammocks and steel doors, waiting for further information. Ted looked up from his bucket, still with a scrubbing brush in hand and produced a long, low whistle. Charlie stood panting and having difficulty catching his breath. "That's one of the reasons you were demoted to lower rope Charlie! Take a deep breath and tell me more." There were faces all around waiting with baited breath for Charlie to calm down and start breathing again. "It's this Friday. I just overheard the Chief. He's been discussing

What… no Donald Duck?

"Er… well, can't they play with their masks on?"

arrangements with the Captain. Jo'burg's mayor or someone wants to impress the Navy." Ted slowly stood up and began to rub his hands together. He knew at that moment that he had been wise to join the Navy to see the world. This was it. This was his chance to make something of himself. This was fortune finally smiling on him.

There was much excited talking and laughing going on amongst the other Boys. Charlie noticed a strange look come over Ted's face though. "I know you always thought it would be a diamond mine Ted, but gold is good enough isn't it?"

Everyone knew Ted's obsession with diamond mines. Ever since he had been selected for the South Africa station Ted had plotted and planned every conceivable variation on one obsessive theme. He had drawn every diagram necessary to fulfill the schemes and secure enough diamonds to live on for the rest of his life.

After supper that evening the Chief mustered the Boys for a 'chat'. "Now Boys, as you know we will be displaying in Jo'burg for Navy Week. By way of a thank you, the mayor has offered you lucky lads a trip to the Robertson Deep Gold Mine. Being three miles down, it is the deepest in the world – not easy to run up from with a pocket full of gold dust! So if you all behave yourselves, the manager *may* allow you into the reserves and actually handle some real-life gold bullion. However if you don't behave yourselves I will leave you down there! You are to wear No. 1s. I want you all on deck for 08:30 … in the morning Slater, ready for role call and bus embarkation".

Ted hardly heard a word the Chief was saying past the bullion comment. He wondered if there might be a wonder cure for tired muscles. All the exercise they had been put through didn't help Ted with his cause. Building muscles was good – it made you strong, not easily bullied and more able to get a rope display right. However, if muscles are tired they are less likely to respond to demands of heavy lifting or running with weights. "I wonder how much a gold bar weighs." Ted mused to himself. "Would one gold bar be equal in value to one large diamond or one small diamond? A diamond is much easier to hide, I know, because I have thought of at least 27 different ways of concealment. Now I will have to start again with gold, and I haven't any time either. Ahh! Of course there may be more chance of finding a nugget or two lying around on the deck of the mine! Humm, now how many nuggets to one bar?" After they had been dismissed Ted wandered off muttering to himself, deep in thought and full of concentration.

The visit to the Robertson Deep Mine passed without incident. Ted felt that his reputation must have preceded him, because there were at least three managers all keeping their beady eyes on him, or so he thought. The floor of the mine was spotless – not even one tiny gold nugget lying about. With a young boy's dreams shattered it just meant that Ted would have to revert back to his diamond heist, and hope they would get an opportunity of a visit to one of those mines.

After the Empire Exhibition, the Boys Division returned to Simonstown and their ship. The normal pre-war cruises around the east and west coasts of Africa continued with the 'showing of the flag' responsibilities. Thus the 1st Lieutenant ordered an extra 'Paint Ship' at Walvis Bay, because there were to be many official calls as far north as Dakar. 'All hands' applied the boiled oil, red lead, flattening and topcoat. This meant officers, stokers and seamen alike. The ship's sides had an ordinary paint and the gun turrets and all superstructures were finished with a very high gloss.

After 48 hours of hard slog, the men and boys finally finished. Their ship was gleaming, looking absolutely immaculate. Now all they had to do was clean themselves up. They needed to dhobey the crab fat from their overalls, strop their clothes out to dry and the paint needed to be scrubbed from their skin. Only then could they all turn in for a well-earned rest.

They slept very well that night, even as a mean easterly wind blew up a storm across the Kalahari Desert – its location immediately due west of Walvis Bay.

The next morning Ted emerged from the messdeck, bleary-eyed but not blind. The ship looked like a colossal Henry Moore sculpture in sandstone, with not a square inch of paint showing. There was sand in every crook and nanny, from truck to keel. As the emerging seamen ran out of expletives so the Kalahari may have run out of sand.

With only one remedy and many sighs, the workforce had to begin again from the scraping down, boiled oil, red lead, flattening and topcoat. Six days later and with a hastily revised schedule the ship was spruce enough to proceed up the west coast on her visits.

Ted has since considered many missed opportunities, one of which being his perfectly sculptured sandstone cruiser. As with conservation of *HMS Belfast* on the Thames reach or as a *piece de resistance* to replace a pile of artistic house bricks at the Tate Gallery, his old ship could have been brought home as a permanent exhibition.

The sailor (?) who thought the 'Beveridge Plan' was the provision of hot oxos for seasick sailors

Naval Terms Illustrated – "Capacity Loaded"

Be Prepared

by Merry Swan

As the boy-sailor matured, he began to believe that playtime in pre-war Africa suited him. With a Royal Naval cruiser squadron and many sporting activities, it all seemed to help Ted stick to the straight and narrow, with a clean nose. There were the coast cruises; but more importantly the boxing, water polo, boat-pulling regattas and sailing races. Then with a month's shooting detail on top of Simonsberg from 06:00 to 12:00 daily, Ted was left clear to indulge in his newfound interest for the afternoons. Having acquired a taste for the odd glass of beer and with no water nearby to swim in, Ted's finances now dictated that he had

Hot dogs from Southend?

to find alternative free entertainment for most of the last month in Africa. He thought that testing his own physical and mental thresholds by climbing, a cheap option for entertainment. Now Ted didn't have a 'stamina training' or 'orienteering' type approach to climbing, just a simple 'get out and do something', 'back in time for tea' outlook.

Having stretched his horizons to climbs around the peninsular in the afternoons, it came to his ship's last weekend at the Cape before departing for the UK at the conclusion of her commission. "I've not attempted the Table Top and we depart on Tuesday. Yeah, but I live in London and have never visited the Tower", he argued with himself. "Well it's now or never". His mind was made up at lunchtime when the cocky leading seaman told him he was a fool. His preparations began in earnest and consisted of pulling his stout parade boots out with some thick woollen socks and his seaman's jumper, intelligently thinking, "It will be a bit colder up on top of the world". Then, borrowing some khaki shorts, he booked himself in for an early sleep at the White Ensign Club in Cape Town and woke to a bright, clear and warm Sunday morning.

"Simonstown Snoopers" Sneak several sections of shore leave in the suburbs of Snoekie! (to sit sipping succulent sups of 'soda water'?)

Following his shave, shampoo and shoeshine Ted needed to shove-off sharpish to catch the 06:00 bus to Kloof-Nek – the highest point by road above Cape Town. After alighting from the bus Ted muttered, "Well this isn't as bad as they have been saying", as he began walking around the foot of the Table for two miles. He then reached a point above Camps Bay and reeled at the sight of a signpost pointing straight up the face of the mountain, "Brinkswater Ravine". "Good joke! Oh well… nothing ventured". With an untroubled conscience Ted commenced his ascend with the bright sunshine warming his back as his whistling echoed through the valley below.

After an hour of reasonably easy climbing Ted began to struggle as the way became steeper and more indistinct. "Why haven't previous walkers left little signs for me – 'foothold here' or 'finger grip there' – most inconsiderate!" Beginning to struggle and slip, Ted needed to stop and think. "Maybe I should have just taken a bus to the coast for a swim…" It was at this moment that he noticed the sound of running water. "Ah ha, water! Water always finds its own level – downhill. So if I follow it upwards, I'll get there!" Ted decided to follow the water route hoping it to be a quicker ascent, albeit wetter. There were many rivulets trickling down offering him many choices.

Unnoticed by Ted, thick sea mist had begun to rise from Camps Bay. The weather had deteriorated rapidly and he was becoming colder and damper. It was only after another hour that Ted realised he couldn't see very much. Visibility had dropped to about five yards. Just enough light to make shapes out, but he *had* to keep going. A table top of clouds had fallen, spreading and rushing to meet the sea mist. Then at last, relief. Ted felt himself level out and realised he was on the Table Top, still surrounded in cloud; then panic. He couldn't see an inch in front of him now and one false move on the edge would send him hurtling back to Camps Bay the fast way.

Ted tortured himself. "My mental machinery has switched to custard". "Why did I decide to do this?" "Why didn't I listen to them?" "Well at least someone will say I *nearly* made it". "Concentrate you idiot!" "No I can't!" "My brain hurts!" "Think, think! …" "OK two options, I can sit it out till the cloud lifts – that may take up to 24 hours. Or I can crawl round the edge till I find the cable-car terminal – no money, could I scrounge a lift down? Ah but the car doesn't operate until Monday. Great either way, how pleased will my Captain be if I returned to the ship 24 hours adrift?" Crouched up in a ball with his head between his hands, Ted contemplated his plight.

"Hall-ooo-oo", "Halloo-oo" came a reply. Kicking his flagging spirits in the posterior Ted quickly 'halloo-oo-ed' back. He sprung onto his knees and began a cautious crawl towards the welcome voices. Like a rising magician through a stage trap door, there stood a scoutmaster, as one by one his scouts joined him in a clearing patch of cloud. Against his juvenile judgement and opposition to any schoolmasters, scoutmasters or parsons, Ted decided he would join the group for a lesson in the art of quick downhill travel via the Platte-Klip.

An hour later, with little material left in the seat of his shorts and through the 'boots, balance and backside' method of decent, Ted joined the scouts for a hot drink around their campfire before everyone dispersed their several ways. Having missed the last bus, Ted welcomed the slow trek back to town just so he could revel in the relief of safety and *terra firma* under his feet. A very welcome bath and meal awaited Ted at the White Ensign Club later that evening.

Part of Ship final preparations began in earnest on Monday. By Tuesday morning, with fond farewells completed, the ship cleared harbour with her Paying Off pendant proudly flying high while the Royal Marine band livened up the proceedings resplendent on the quarterdeck.

Ted had recuperated well and was back to his 'dodging' average. After a rushed messdeck scrub out before the Petty Officer began to circulate, Ted spread the morning's Cape Times out on the lockers for a quick read. His brain suffered a sudden and absolute energy crisis as it came to a shuddering halt. Front-page news – a young couple had started to climb up the Table Top Mountain on Sunday. They were still stranded somewhere, over 48 hours later. A search and rescue party were looking for them even as Ted's ship cleared False Bay on its homeward journey.

Ted learnt a couple of things from his jaunt. He has never climbed alone since, and in the truest sense of the words, he has followed the scout motto "Be prepared".

"… and this one lost his glasses"

Galloping round Ganges

From Ipswich Town to Shotley Gate – as you travel down the road –
with kit bag, case and hammock – quite a heavy load.
Up against the skyline – standing clear – the mast –
of wooden ships and iron men – part of Navy's past.

Greeted by the Gate Staff – and 'Crushers' One and Two –
'Lift and Shift', don't dawdle – or they will scream at you.
Then right there before you – as 'Crushers' draft chit take –
one hundred and fifty foot of mast – stands beside that gate.

This you'll get to know quite well – in later days whilst there –
up ratlines and futtock rigging – you will not turn a hair.
Perhaps as part of competition – as any 'sprog' will know –
or, quiet bet on a messmate's tot – your prowess hope to show.

The Wardroom Mess was also game – to gallop up and down –
especially after Guest Night – or night out in the town.
Once or twice saw 'raff types' – and 'brown jobs' up there too –
they never beat the Wardroom – in this 'Old Time Navy Do'.

Check on each Division – and 'Nozzers' cross the road –
each against each other – in strictest discipline code.
Names of famous Admirals – crowding in on me –
Grenville, Drake and Nelson – those masters of the sea.

My Sailors

Be bloody, bold and resolute – just like Admiral Blake –
take sailing crew of 'juniors' – down to Shotley 'Lake'.
Carry out all boat drills – lowering of both falls –
ship the mast, hoist the sails – check all boats re-calls.

Cast off in a hurry – point up in the stream –
boat handling by some 'juniors' – makes you want to scream.
Watch the other boats just here – reach the starting line –
manage to get thereabouts – as the gun goes just in time.

Into the gymnasium – Divisional Boxing Night –
swift weigh-in – lace on gloves – prove that you can fight.
Flounder through a round or two – scowl as thick as sin –
opponent just as green as you – this one you can win.

Knots and splices – ropes and yarns – nimble fingers needed now –
got to get all this lot right – and pass exam somehow.
Steel wire hawsers, marlinspikes – and tools of the trade –
splicing, serving, whipping – this is no masquerade.

Box the compass, steer a steady – ring down two more knots –
ship handling and ship husbandry – signals, dash and dots.
Sweep horizon, keep sharp lookout – is that a lighthouse glim?
Keep on with work – stay alert – a seaman can't be dim.

Boat-work in the Orwell, and up and down the Stour –
this should be quite enjoyable – did some of this before.
But not with 18 ft of ash – and back that's fit to break –
commands and shouts and blasphemy – I find this hard to take.

Sailing though is better – when balmy breezes blow –
but not the 5-mile boat-pull home – you're not allowed a tow.
'Square up' in the boat – and secure it for the night –
quick snack meal – flake out on bed – in early evening light.

Naval Terms Illustrated – "Squalls Imminent"

Football, hockey, rugger – games are always on –
especially those against the Staff – play in every one.
Get a chance to dig them hard – or crack a shin or two –
but watch it close – they may have got – their beady eye on you.

In and out of Swimming Bath – with water polo ball –
swimming, diving, training – this sport is best of all.
Competitions and some matches – sweep away all fears –
will he finish up 'water-logged' and wet behind the ears?

Athletics in the summer – some training on the track –
Starts and relay takeovers – sprint – but don't look back.
Mums and Dads and girlfriends there – but check their sisters too –
maybe there's a dolly-bird – who is just right for you.

Rifle drill and square-bashing – marching up and down –
keep in time – get it right – or curtailed trips to town.
As 'jankers' then for 14 days – you'll be your messmates' pride –
Are you fit? Can you run? Can you take this in your stride?

Laundry Hill may ring a bell – with one or two of you –
this was part of 'jankers' hell – if you're in that little crew.
Then of course depends how tight – your halo round your neck –
Were you man? Were you mouse? Or just a physical wreck?

Oh to be a knight on a sailor like this!

Draft Chit (1)
by Merry Swan

It was October 1939. Ted thought he and the other two new Pompey qualifiers would get a chance to idle in their barracks following their year of hard physical training work and examinations. No chance – the phoney part of World War II, the early months, saw those in charge believing the threat of gas warfare would continue on from WWI. Therefore the three new Royal Navy PT qualifiers were put to immediate use and sent to Tipnor firing range just on the outskirts of Portsmouth, to procure further qualifications as gas instructors.

At the range the three men climbed from the back of the truck at the end of a long lane leading up and out of sight. There was a barrier across the track, with one sentry inside a small wooden hut. Wrapped up in a great-coat over his uniform and a knitted scarf, he opened the door outwards and addressed the men, "Name? OK, wait there. Name? OK wait there. Name? Right I am going to give you all instructions on how to reach your temporary barracks. Under no circumstances will you vary from them, even if Hitler himself distracts you." He then carried on in a boring tone.

Setting off along the winding track with kitbags slung over their shoulders, they could see the red flags were flying. These flags indicated varying degrees of gas bombs being or to be exploded. The amigos hadn't noticed the stiff breeze blowing across the heath land as they chatted and ribbed each other on the virtues of childhood stink bombs. They discussed varying methods of assembly and successfulness, compared with stinkers bought in their local joke shop.

The barracks were as the men had come to expect – bare floor boards, basic iron-framed beds, folded horsehair mattresses, one striped pillow and two regulation-issue dark grey blankets per bed with a tall wooden cupboard next to each bed. The washhouse was located next door.

The following morning all the new trainees were gathered in the makeshift classroom of a Nissan hut. There were neat rows of very old-looking wooden school desks with wooden benches in between. There was enough room for three people to sit on one form and share two desks. The officer in charge opened the door, stepped in and addressed them with a very authoritative voice. "Right men, at ease. This course you have all been sent on is of vital importance to the war effort. You will be instructed in all aspects of gas warfare. Your job will be to facilitate all members of His Majesty's forces to have correctly fitted gas masks, to be acquainted with their respirators and for them to be able to use them. You will also need to recognise the enemy's known chemical agents and take necessary lifesaving precautions. At no time are you to think this is going to be easy – understand?" "Yes Sir". The reply came in unison. The officer instructed the men to sit as he turned to the easel with a blackboard, looking for some chalk.

Many of the classroom days continued in silence from the floor, with various instructors, diagrams and stories spewing out from the front platform. Outdoor instruction days rolled on regardless of the weather. The men needed to be familiar with the varying warning smells and skin reactions of enemy gases, which meant being exposed to different chemical agents. They wore thick gloves as they worked their way along the trestle tables, cautiously sniffing the different wooden boxes in front of them. Then there were the days of short marches through the Range where gas-warning flags would suddenly be deployed. "If I have to put this respirator on one more time before tea, I'll go mad," Ted complained. He was trying to finish a whole sentence without interruption, not that Joe seemed interested in the African PT displays Ted had been describing with some flourish. In fact Joe was definitely distracted with something in his boot. He dropped to the ground and rapidly untied his laces, then pulled at his boot sides with some vigour. The boot came flying off and Joe then tugged hard at his woollen sock. Sam and Ted had pulled over from the others by this time. "My chilblains are giving me some right gyp suddenly." Joe's toes were very red and sore looking. Sam offered some friendly advice as he collected Joe's boot for him. "You didn't use enough phoo-phoo dust on ya feet this morning Joe! Now hurry, the instructor hasn't noticed we're not still with them. We might just have time to get back into some semblance of order." Ted mocked, "You'll be alright Joe, we're doing 'life saving precautions' on Friday. I'll save you then!" as they all walked over the hill to the next obstacle. By the time they were back to Barracks that afternoon, Joe was hobbling quite badly. That evening Joe was unceremoniously shipped off to Haslar RNH with a seriously poisoned foot.

Because the gas course was rapidly drawing to a close, three days later a draft chit arrived for Joe. Thoughtful Ted, being of the same Mess in barracks as his sick colleague, scrawled across the chit, "Ha, ha … sick – Haslar" and returned it to the drafting office. Their sense of humour prevailed and the same chit was returned to the Mess with 'Sick – Haslar' struck through, the words 'Ha, ha' underlined and Ted's name substituted in lieu of his colleague's name! Ted went to his next posting with a chip on his shoulder because the drafter had a better sense of humour than he, and his mate had managed to 'dodge the draft'.

After WWII Ted thought it was time to get rid of his chip and find out what happened to his bath-steward of a colleague. He soon found the answer as his mate had swapped ships and taken Ted's draft in *HMS Express* – as noted on the Roll of Honour in the entrance hall of the PT School in Portsmouth.

Ted feels he has been living on borrowed time ever since.

Ode to Hedging your Bet

For those of us – who think we're great,
What happens at the Pearly Gate?
Our previous mates – I'm sure have spoken
For the PT Branch – it's bound to open.

On the other hand – if we're accused
Of the things in life – which we've abused,
We'll get a Draft Chit – down to Hell
There'll be a PT Branch – down there as well.

Body in the Bag

by Merry Swan

Wartime Britain offered a stable mooring for Ted as he looked over his shoulder at the ship. A yawning hole forward of the bridge drew his night terrors alive with a shudder. "Not a bowl of cherries" he thought and quickened his pace to the dockyard barrier. A bitter wind on a cold morning took him straight to the transport waiting – a bus to regular meals, a dry bed and Shangri-La.

Anticipation grew for the scruffy young Naval seaman as each mile took him closer to the newly equipped gymnasium, large playing field

Don't speak to the cad … he's a rank outsidah-h!

and best of all the swimming baths. "Football, rugby, swimming, water polo – what a glorious change to have my feet on *terra firma*" Ted inwardly smiled.

Following Ted's new-post fever, there came many new routines to deal with and new officers to avoid. Happily he met a like-minded sporting fellow early on, who worked in the Stores as a butcher, but played a mean game of football and rugby, so was duly selected, along with Ted, for 'friendlies' against the Marines. Their friendship grew as each match passed, and their reputation grew as each celebratory or commiserative drink passed.

As Ted and Butch piled loudly into the bar, a table of Marines looked up and stared. "Ah Landlord, two pints of your very best please, in celebration. We slaughtered them good this time!" heckled Butch. One Marine jumped out of his chair sending it clattering to the floor. Hands curling and tightening, Ted straightened and paused. All eyes were now lunging towards the Marine, who sensed a chance to unwind from the stresses of the day. "We'll have you rotten lot – make no mistake," he blurted as he flew towards them, fists raised. Ted's body dropped as he stood firm ready for the onslaught. Two sailors looked up from their shove ha'penny board and saw the 'game' was on. Bodies, fists, furniture all started to mix into a mess of sounds.

Ted's left eye swollen with pleasure began to beat with pain as the military policeman dragged him out onto the pavement. "Right you're nicked. Breach of the peace and disorderly conduct", he snapped. "Bang goes my Good Conduct badge" Ted sighed quietly, as he resigned himself to being frog-marched back to camp.

With no more leave available for a while, Ted threw himself into work. Extra trapeze training meant extra swims when he missed a catch of the pole. When swimming, he just wanted to scale the ropes to the trapeze platform and try again. "An endless circle of hard work" he chuckled. Then it sprang into his head, "My chance to get some leave for Christmas! Get a rope and ladder display team back together, for the morale of the Establishment. A brilliant idea for my Petty Officer to have, and I might just be able to swing it in time".

An Aladdin's Cave of tinned food and other rations on the physical training establishment were available at greatly reduced prices for officers

Naval Terms Illustrated – "Top Hampered"

"Sit down Clubs – remember giving me out LBW last Wednesday?"

and their wives who lived off camp – but not for ratings like Ted living 'in'. However, friendships were to be greatly savoured, and strong sportsmen bonds more so for Ted. "Butch, you've got to help me. I've got some leave in three days time. I haven't seen my poor ol' Mum and sisters for two years now, and it's nearly Christmas. I want to take them something really special". Ted stepped closer and in loud whispers began to explain his plan to Butch.

On the morning of his leave, Ted resplendent in best uniform, leave pass, travel warrant, large green suitcase and a small brown weekend case, presented himself to the beef-screen. He passed the brown, empty case to Butch and onto the deck relieved himself of the larger, heavy case with triangulated corners of canvass. Butch gave Ted a quick nod, opened the screen and took the case. Before Ted had a chance to double-check for 'visitors', Butch dived into a walk-in freezer and retrieved a side of beef.

He then sculptured a block to the exact size of the case, wrapped it in greaseproof paper, and then shoehorned it in to the case.

Without a stitch extra to wear and no toothbrush, Ted weight-lifted his gold dust to the camp perimeter and the beginning of his long journey home. The bus into the city was no problem but then came the traverse to

"But Sir – when good rum goes into plum duff it IS a 'special' occasion!"

the railway station. Ted was almost reeling under the weight of his cases by the time he had negotiated the heavy traffic, steps and bridges over the platforms and the bustle of people at the station. After a juggling act with his leave pass, travel warrant and cases at the barrier, he finally mounted the train step and bumped his way to an empty compartment. Kicking the door aside with his foot Ted collapsed into a seat before standing again and stowing his haul in the luggage racks.

The eight-hour rail journey began as a much-needed rest for Ted until a slight panic began to set in as a drop of water falling on his head stirred him. He slowly opened his eyes as he became aware of other people now crowding his compartment. "Wow, it's suddenly become very warm in here" he thought, not realising he had been asleep for nearly seven hours. He casually lifted up his wrist and glanced at his watch. An energy crisis enveloped Ted as his heart did a tango. "The meat is defrosting and bleeding onto my head!" he screamed to himself. Ted's brain nearly shuddered to a halt as the train pulled into a station. He quickly rallied and jumped to attention, made his apologies to his travelling companions then made a grab for his cases.

"One more stop till I can escape" Ted reminded himself, standing in the corridor of the train with his bleeding case on top of the other, hoping the blood would not show. The train finally steamed into Kings Cross, slowly and hope above all hopes, surely. But as Ted peered out of the window his eyes grabbed sight of Service police doing their two-by-two march past. He knew he had to become clever; really clever now. As he grabbed for the suitcase handles, he stared at the floor of the corridor and quickly did a couple of steps of the Highland reel to erase any telltale rivulets of blood.

Suddenly the train threw its contents about violently; Ted opened the door and threw himself out, suitcases in tow. Before the train driver knew he had stopped, Ted high-tailed himself and his contraband to the barrier, his eyes wildly shooting around for the military. Somehow, he managed to appear calm, cool and collected while he lumped his cases down at the barrier and showed his passes.

Quickly Ted ran out of the station towards the black snake of cars. "Taxi, taxi!" he shouted as he headed towards the line, cases dragging his arms. "Waterloo station, as quick as you like" he requested of a driver, as he approached him. After stowing his stash in the luggage bay, he jumped into the passenger compartment. As Ted felt a sigh of relief envelope him, he noticed a trickle of blood escaping near his canvass-cornered case in the front. "Is the town traffic heavy today?" he almost shouted to the driver.

"Here we are Jack," said the driver calmly. Ted rumbled in his pocket ferociously and pulled out a couple of coins. Stabbing them towards the driver, he absentmindedly told him to keep the change. Waterloo station seemed to Ted like a whole military police camp. Everywhere he looked there were red and white caps, somehow marching in squadrons through the crowded throng of other uniforms. He caught sight of a public convenience sign and tried to head directly for it, head lowered in order to avoid any piercing eye contact. To his right he heard a shrill voice shout "Daily Mirror, get ya' Daily Mirror 'ere!"

He negotiated the steps down to the toilets, struggling not to drop his newly purchased paper. After finding an empty cubicle, he forewent the 'Jane' strip cartoon for the cause, opened the little case and padded it out to absorb the blood. Ted sat down for a minute and took a deep breath.

The last leg of the journey was now upon Ted, as he sat on the train to Portsmouth. This time though he placed the offending cases in the corridor and took a corner seat so he could keep his beady eye on them. As his mental machinery began to function again, he decided to avoid more Naval patrols at the town stop, and remained on the train right through to Portsmouth harbour. It was late in the evening as the train shunted to a stop, so Ted deposited his cases in the left luggage and explained to the elderly porter that he would collect them early the following morning.

After a fitful sleep in one of the homely armchairs, Ted crept out of the house before anyone had stirred and headed down to the harbour station for the last stage of his operation. This was going to take all his best social skills, Ted thought dubiously to himself. However, when he arrived at the hatch he spotted a pool of blood by his cases. He quickly plunged in to engage the porter with some scintillating conversation. Then with a sideward step and the *coup de grace*, Ted suggested that he should shift the 'very heavy' cases himself. He handed over the left-luggage tickets, dived in, grabbed them and high-tailed it to the nearest taxi rank, then on to the safety of his dear old Mum.

Ted thought the whole escapade was well worthwhile, as he laid the cases on the kitchen table and opened them up. Faces of delight peered in. His Mum and sisters were to survive the worst of the wartime rationing with many tins of food for the months following and a splendid piece of beef for Christmas. "Thanks Butch".

Ode to a (PT Branch) Schoolie

Muscle-bound – for years and years,
Always was – between the ears.
Grey matter now – has to be used,
Muscle-bound – I'm still accused.

Oi ... Watch it .. Clubs

As she came to me – that night –
her clothes about her were quite tight.
My eyes they popped – I stood and stared –
as gracefully her limbs she bared.

A smile, a nod, and all was well –
I had her in my magic spell.
Now I'd force my will on her –
in much a way she'd not deter.

Bouncing, bubbling, beaming beauty –
curvy, cuddly, gleaming cutie.
Out to show what she can do –
she may even try the same with you.

Her swaying body – swirling arms –
movements to enhance her charms.
She pressed, she pushed, she pulled around –
with that 'heavy breathing' sound.

She pouted, postured, pranced about –
in such a way, I'd almost shout.
She squealed, she squirmed, she asked for more –
whilst exercising on the floor.

Draft Chit (2)

by Merry Swan

So here was Ted, a 'no-badge' killick, on a Pompey built, bought and manned ack-ack cruiser, *HMS Sirius*. The ship's commission had been taking in many Mediterranean sights from the African west coast runs, past Gibraltar, through Malta's Ohio convoy to Bone in Algiers, then some invading of Sicily and Italy and a Salerno skylark and on to the Dodecanese islands. Unfortunately this is where Ted's ship caught a 250lb bomb on her quarterdeck, making part of her look rather untidy.

For repairs, his Lords' Commissioners in their wisdom decided on three alternative places – the UK, the USA or Massawa on the Red Sea.

"Ah hmm!... I'll get the boys to start reprisal raids!"

"But Sir! My Heath-Atkinson mark IV will definitely revolutionise ack-ack fire!"

They settled on the ship going to Massawa, not far off the equator. This would mean that the Ship's Company would spend three weeks per month at the base and need to spend another week each month in the hills to recuperate.

Now during all of this commission Ted's GC badges had suffered and it became known throughout the Ship's Company that he only ever seemed to go ashore once every 6 months; even though Ted doubled up as 'captain of the gun' and he believed he organised his job well.

Following the completion of repairs to *HMS Sirius*, after the ship had left Massawa and was entering the Suez Canal, Ted was summonsed to the Captain. This was a place well known to Ted, but nearly always for the wrong reasons – a bit like being called to the headmaster's study for a caning. He normally got hauled up like this after failing to impress the military police with his fists, when on shore leave for a couple of hours. While racking his brains as to any misdemeanours he may have committed, Sam began pulling Ted's leg again. Ted had learnt not to take the bait from his mess mates anymore as it only ended in a punch-up with him always being caught and blamed.

Allied Landing in North Africa "All ashore who're going ashore!"

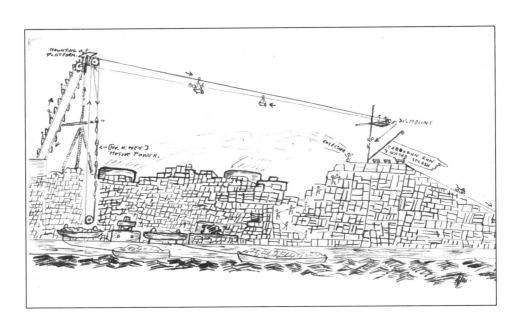

(Suggestion for 'Store Ship Sirius' scenic railway)
"The Sirius Star outshines the lot, but the Sirius ship is best in dock.
There she lay with good support, made from the steel that 'Pompey' bought.
Now the Sirius in all her splendour, is only used as a *cargo tender*."

Having changed into number one uniform, Ted grabbed his cap and put it on, making sure it was straight and secure. Ted did not want more misery on his broad shoulders so he quickly made his way from the foc'stle, then round and down aft to the captain's quarters. On arrival at the correct gangway he reported to the Master at Arms and waited in line with a few other quiet souls.

He always imaged it hilarious to 'knock' at the captain's doorway – there was normally a dull, grey Navy-issued curtain across the gangway to the captain's table. People would have to rap their knuckles hard on the bulkhead to get anyone's attention and that would be before punishments commenced! However, the Chief made the announcements for each allotted timed-appointment, so everyone's knuckles were safe.

Now it transpired that Ted was to see the Captain to have his Petty Officer's rate restored. Unfortunately in the excitement Ted found himself in the unusual position of standing before that deity with his cap *on*. However, nothing daunted and with his usual panache, Ted asked the Commander, "And how long will I keep the PO rate this time, Sir?" The Commander being equal to the occasion replied, "All the time you are on this ship. We finish the Canal passage and enter Alexandria tomorrow morning. Pack your kitbag and hammock. YOU'RE DRAFTED!"

Naval Terms Illustrated – "A Run Ashore"

"He's gnu!"

Jack Ashore
or
Butterfly Badges

Along the road – two sailor lads –
one sunny day were walking.
And as they walked – with smile and grin –
in mouthy strain were talking –

About this run ashore that day –
and where to trap some lasses.
They went gaily on their way –
to try some dancing classes.

So they walked – a fair old stretch –
and walking – still grew frisky.
From time to time – from lip to lip –
they passed a bottle of whisky.

At last they reached a little village –
their hall was used for dancing.
Like Vikings of old – on rape and pillage –
twas here they would do their prancing.

Classes here were in full swing –
with loads of village lovelies.
Some to farmer's boy would cling –
whilst others had their hubbies.

Signal Terms Illustrated – "Down of all …"

Now Jack – when he's ashore at times –
often lacks a little finesse –
And being used to foreign climes –
will bulldoze with the best.

Heaving sacks of wheat with pride –
and bales of hay at harvest –
Makes chest the size of cow's backside –
and biceps – most the largest.

When wine is in – sense has flown –
and Jack should heed this warning –
Shoulders like boulders these men have grown –
and could barely stifle yawning.

As Jack is shortly in full sail –
with mouth and fancy antic –
Wives and girlfriends going pale –
tell partners they're getting frantic.

Shortly then – around young Jack –
descends some muscle – on the hoof.
Fists start flying – Jack on back –
then heaved up through tin roof.

Farmers ensure – there is no spoof –
and heave them through the skylight.
Sliding down on outside roof –
Jack prays that all will come right.

Not a chance – the angled roof –
is poised above a pigpen.
As they slide – they need no proof –
in trough they land – quite shaken.

Hasty retreat – whilst all forlorn –
thus ends this little spree.
Shattered and tattered, tired and torn –
and stinking – up to knee.

Wend their weary homeward way –
to ship – laying in the docks.
Expect the loss of lots of pay –
for not pulling up their socks.

Skipper's heard it all before –
their halo's far from tight.
Besides the pay – jankers they score –
and stay aboard each night.

Now all you Jolly Sailor Lads –
just heed this shellback's mutter.
Stay aboard – don't act like cads –
badges, hooks and rates will flutter.

"- MORE ROPE!!"

Ode to GC Badges

Badges come, badges go –
On the 'skate' they're known to 'flutter'.
In later years, his mouth would hold –
Great big lumps of farmhouse butter.

"Quick … take my photo whilst I've still got them!"

51

Father Christmas Has Middle Watch

by Merry Swan

As Joe had dodged his draft with a poisoned foot, Ted had to take his place. The young Leading Seaman (PT branch) joined a Tribal Class destroyer, *HMS Cossack*, up in Rosyth, Ted's first visit to Scotland. Many nautical miles were covered as some historic and notable events unfolded. The ship's First Lieutenant was changed between the Altmark incident in March 1940 and the second battle of Narvik that April. Ted now found

"Ya Herr Lieut'nt, bail where?"

himself with a very ambitious, young two-striper, who had been spotlighted for promotion and was already pushing for his half-stripe and for his own command. The new Lieutenant ran a taut ship along with the four-striped skipper. In addition to normal wartime hazards, he kept the Ship's Company very much on their toes.

The whole flotilla ploughed the furrow on Christmas Eve. The standard in these situations was for the ammunition numbers of the guns' crew to provide lookouts on the bridge. This applied to the leading ship of the squadron, at the point of the 'V'. So there were port and starboard lookouts from the gun's crew out on the exposed bridge wings of the Cruising Station watch, which included Ted as captain of a 4.7-inch gun. The new 1st Lieutenant was closing up for Middle Watch to take over the con and relieve the Gunnery Officer, who was standing down. The Lieutenant took the position, course, zigzag times and all relevant points at his turnover allowing the Gunner to go below for a well-earned kip.

Despite some Ship's Company's ideas and Ted's in particular, the new Lieutenant was human. Although there was a reduced watch the Lieutenant

"It's their new First Lieutenant – I spotted him just now!"

53

was going to wish his personnel on the bridge a happy Christmas. He stepped down from the captain's stool ten minutes into Christmas day and began to circulate. There he exchanged greetings with the Petty Officer of the Watch, the Signalman, the Messenger and the port lookout.

A slow, easy movement at sea can be monotonous and tiring, especially if you are on a lookout trick. However the last thing to do is hunch up and rest your binoculars on the sponsors, with your eyes glued against the lenses. Ted had dozed off in what appeared to be an attentive position. As the Lieutenant circled in the starboard lookout's position, he kept the normal quiet, calm voice of a person on Middle Watch and leant over the side of the bridge, "Starboard lookout – A happy Christmas". Receiving no reply, the Lieutenant, in a louder voice, said, "Starboard lookout?" Then leaning right over he gave Ted a shake by the shoulder, "Starboard lookout – a happy Christmas – and place yourself on report, for being asleep on Watch".

Years later in Malta, Ted met his 1st Lieutenant again. However the 1st Lieutenant now had four stripes and Ted declined to explain why half his old Ship's Company used to called him Father Christmas.

Pompey and the Dockyard Ditty

Girls parading Guildhall Square –
all teeth and smiles and blonded hair.
Matelots pass – on evening out –
jest and jibe – and give loud shout.

In that same Square – strain more and more –
to hear those Guildhall lions roar.
When 'ere a virgin hove in sight –
stony silence – every night.

"… and it always smells rather fishy round here!"

Dockyard round the edge of town –
cranes and trucks – ply up and down.
Stand well clear – as they pass by –
clothes well splashed and mud in eye.

Gates to dockyard open wide –
Nelson's Victory – just inside.
Renowned of course – this famous name –
reminder of Old England's fame.

Masts and rigging – wooden spars –
bare foot sailors – Jolly Tars.
From sail to steam was quite a step –
modern change – not over yet.

Joining shackles, joggle shackles, standing pile on pile –
cables large, cables small, stretch for mile on mile.
Wooden ships, iron men, once it was the cry –
now iron ships, modern men, hunt for 'pie in sky'.

"HEY-- WHAT ARE YOU GOING TO DO WITH THOSE?"
"FENDERS -- SKIMMER!"

Sail lofts, canvas, blue lined, neat –
"Don't stand on that – with your plates of meat".
Stretch two bolts and take a measure –
side curtains here – the wardroom's pleasure.

Round seams, flat seams, steady stitching –
if females did this – more bewitching.
Baggy wrinkles, crinkles – reef points –
no doubt – older sails are all blown out.

Cracked and mossy – red tiled roofing –
need some extra weatherproofing.
Corrugated, rusted, ridged and rotten –
stained and dirty at the bottom.

"D'y' hear there? Stop making smoke…"

Dockyard maties walk around –
wellie boots make scuffling sound.
Flat cloth cap, fearnought jacket –
whining drill and riveting racket.

Scrawny moggies – slinking round –
scrounging snacks in ships' boat pound.
Descendants of old time ships' cats –
waging war on mice and rats.

Always worth a meal or two –
to visit ships that're passing through.
As lock is opened – leave newfound chum –
rush ashore – in scrambling run.

Rough and rutted road, with railway track –
Stores train passing – clickety clack.
Vital parts – for ships in dock –
gun barrels, bearings, davit blocks.

Dockyard police – searching hard –
matelots – passing through the yard.
As they step ashore each night –
palpitations – awful fright.

Overhead on jetty – crane jibs swinging –
sailors return from shore – all singing.
Stumbling walk – but feeling fine –
hope they all get aboard – on time.

Wrens near offices – sometimes seen –
sharp-eyed matelot – awfully keen.
Especially when just in from sea –
views ankle, calf, and shapely knee.

Tides that rip, tides that flow –
tides creeping over mud flats – slow.
Whilst dog watch sailing – for a little skylark –
high and dry – become Pompey mud lark.

Then of course – see boats recall –
this dog watch sailing – no good at all.
Beetle browed Commander – takes dim view –
restricts your 'runs ashore' – for a week or two.

Ode to the Ordinary Seaman

Now that you're in the Royal Navy,
It's the 'Rolling Stockist – who gathers no gravy'.
Love them proper – drop them flat,
Push off quick – in your 'bells' and round hat.

Royal Tournament

A Tournament in those days of yore –
could unseat a knight from horse to floor.
Lying prone – in flaked out state –
carried from joust – on five-barred gate.

Armour dented like sardine tin –
could completely crush – and ruin him.
Tin opener worked by willing aide –
ensures that master's life is saved.

'Champion at Arms' is still the thing –
no longer in the jousting ring.
Dismounted now – on fencing piste –
matelots chance will not be missed.

".. and may I introduce our fencing master!"

But Tournament still is yearly run –
for Service charities – and lots of fun.
Larger jousts – and large displays –
the Services in their halcyon days.

We had no horses – to pull our guns –
say field-guns' crew – the muscle-bound ones.
Flying Angel will always be –
like Tarzan swinging in jungle tree.

"Unlimber – off wheels – through the wall" –
duck down low – if you are tall.
"On wheels – limber up"- scrambling run –
"Action front" – three shots, from each gun.

Motorcycles were once – all over the place –
Signal Corp display – was no disgrace.
Nineteen piled on one small bike –
Me? – I'm chicken – I'd rather hike.

"He's been like that since we saw the Bertram Mills Show …"

"Yeah! He's their wheel number going through the wall!"

High box and chair tricks – we've done before –
miss your 'front' – crash on the floor.
It may hurt a bit – but don't give a hoot –
bad knee and ankle – and bandaged foot.

Weeks and months of gymnasium work –
sweating brow and soaking shirt.
Straining, striving every day –
to make your show the best display.

Ropes and window-ladders – is another scene –
for this event – you must be keen.
"Top odds – reverse – and 'swallow' down" –
check rope hard – or 'crumpled crown'.

Drill squad – Royal Marines – smart and sharp –
drop a bayonet – in the cart.
Precision marching – nice to see –
pointed toe – and bended knee.

RHA – with gun carriages – galloping –
horses respond – or – get a larruping.
Manoeuvres fast – the tricky bit –
miss those 'scissors' – you're in the… grit.

Massed Highland Bands – their bagpipes screeching –
headache, eardrums – all beseeching.
"Peace and quiet – for goodness' sake" –
reverberations from domed roof – hard to take.

Royal Air Force also had display –
band accompaniment – every day.
With RAF march past – they'd always plough in –
repeated so often – an awful din.

Memories flash across my mind –
"Were Staff Instructors always kind?"
For me – these days are now long gone –
armchair, slippers, and 'box' – my song.

"Booked any good reds lately?"

Tart of my Heart

January's girl is pale of face –
she doesn't dress in silks and lace.
Wellies, furs and mufflers too –
with all that snow – so should you.

The February girl will soon be seen –
in false eyelash and Nivea cream.
Valentine twangs a Cupid's bow –
Leap Year gets her man – somehow.

The March girl springs in – with the spring –
and flits about like bird on wing.
But watch her where she comes to roost –
she may give your ego a boost.

April's girl so full of pranks –
can cause disturbance in the ranks.
Bachelor boy – don't be conceited –
your status soon may be defeated.

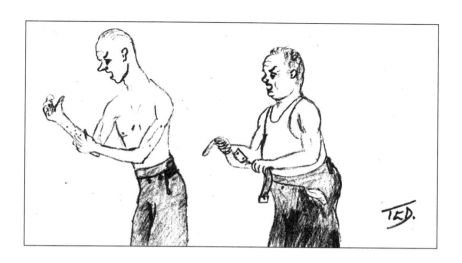

"Did you get bitten last night?"
"No … I got stung though!"

The girl for May – with flowers so gay –
will have you name the wedding day.
Play it smartish – don't be late –
pack your bags and emigrate.

The girl for June – is bursting out –
watch yourself when she's about.
Treat her gently – don't go daft –
arrange yourself a foreign draft.

July girl – of sunny nature –
will get you in her clutch – I betcha.
Never mind – just don't delay –
shoot off quick on holiday.

Naval Terms Illustrated – "Free board"

August girl – like luscious peach –
laps up sun – on crowded beach.
Needs some help – with suntan oil? –
my chance has come – no real toil.

September girl – so full of grace –
returns to work – at lazy pace.
But dreams of holidays – yet to come –
and wanders through her day – humdrum.

October girl in autumn tints –
seldom takes romantic hints.
Bulldoze in – to love at last –
often ends – with murky past.

November girl with rosy cheeks –
will hibernate – for weeks and weeks.
Watch her when she does emerge –
start right in – with her basic urge.

December girl – so prim and smug –
settles in – the hostelry snug.
Knocks back gin – and vodka too –
just to see her Christmas through.

"You and your left fork at the next crossroads…"

Ode to the British Weather

Rain and snow and slush and ice –
Travel to work – not very nice.
Now the weekend comes again –
Then it's snow and slush and rain.

Matelots Terms of Endearment
or
Communications

I speak a little slowly – I suffer from a stutter –
it's always hard to articulate – I nearly always mutter.
I've worked on board – I've done my whack – whilst hosing down the
deck –
water swathed on rolled up trouser, shout "WHAT THE F...... HECK?"

On f'cstle part of ship – one time – as their locker-man –
I'd look after all their shackles, strops and soft-soap in a can.
Each piece was marked – POs got narked when caught with wrongful
stores –
I'd point it out – I'd give loud shout – "THIS F.... THING AIN'T YOURS".

I'd walk around each part of ship – and see what was in use –
I'd keep my council rather quiet – not join in much abuse.
I'd check all scrubbers, brooms and buckets – whenever things were
slack –
spotting one that didn't belong – shout – "BRING THAT B*STARD BACK".

Whilst sailing in the harbour – round Durban – once or twice –
plenty of sun – loads of fun – memorable day – quite nice.
Prepare to go alongside – marked boathook – Bowman – THICK...
Hang on to shroud – shout aloud – "DROP THAT B*STARD – QUICK".

My charms soon fail – luck runs out – when ere it comes to Cupid –
two girls to meet – on quiet run – mine's the 'VG Stupid'.
Being jollied by my mate – with mine – accused of moping –
"PACK IT UP – LEAVE IT OUT – YOU MUST BE F….. JOKING".

When standing rounds on messdeck – polished, scrubbed – quite nice –
tin gear, fanny, cutlery – but hide the poker dice.
Gleaming scuttles – burnished deadlights, all polished at the back –
wrong marked bucket under table – yell – "SHIFT THAT B*STARD, JACK".

Whilst passing through the Topmens Mess – an argument on girls –
how blue her eyes – how round her thighs – her teeth like shiny pearls.
Let them know a thing or three – taxidermist phrase when huffed –
stalk from messdeck – feeling niggled – " YOU F…… LOT GET
STUFFED".

Heard in the Blackout #1

Heard in the Blackout #2

Heard in the Blackout #3

Dreams and the Dreamer (3)

Working up aloft at times – with marlinspike and hammer –
clout my thumb – let out yell – mongst all that working clamour.
Then of course – it slips from grasp – in voice as loud as thunder –
to anyone who's down below – "OI ..B*STARD – STAND FROM
UNDER".

Harbour lights – a run ashore – after all that working –
with my chum – get shifted quickly – I know he's been shirking.
Whilst drinking beer in pub with mate – next round – he's dodging
paying –
shout "OFF F..... QUICK" – REARRANGE THOSE WORDS –
IN A WELL KNOWN PHRASE OR SAYING.

"Do you keep a cat on this messdeck?"

"Make fast and allow for the tide"

Water Carnival

by Merry Swan

In 1952 as a Physical Training Instructor in the Royal Navy, Ted was responsible for the gymnasium and Swimming Bath at Pitt Street, Portsmouth. This suited him admirably as it was now legal for him to be in and out of the water several times a day. The best and most relaxing times though were always the scrubbing out period on a Friday afternoon in the gymnasium, and Saturday mornings in the Swimming Bath.

The first of the Wrens' sports courses were inaugurated about this time. They would complete their short course and then get caught up on their last Friday afternoon with a certain amount of hosing down in the gymnasium. This skylark would always seem to erupt into and around the edges of the Swimming Bath, next door. The Wrens were determined to get a number of Staff Instructors into the pool fully booted. They were achieving some success, when one of them approached Ted. "I think I'm resisting fairly well" Ted thought, as she wrestled with him. Ted could see other Wrens approaching, so did an unchivalrous thing. With a hip-throw and bumps-a-daisy he managed to deposit five of the eight Wrens into the water, fully clothed. For a quick change of tack, Ted then voluntarily dived in to demonstrate his life saving techniques.

Archie, one of the other Instructors, was not in a position to aid or abet Ted, as he was himself surrounded by a wall of giggling dolly-Wrens, enjoying the harassment of dampening his ardour. Unbeknownst to both of them though, Commander Snape was down the corridor and could hear the giggles and screams. Not being adverse to a shapely female, the Commander meandered through to the Bath with a quiet smirk on his

face. Slowly climbing the stairs and unseen by the furore, Snape slid onto a front row seat in the balcony above the swing doors at the shallow end of the pool.

In a sudden moment of clarity, Archie managed to reverse the harassment and began chasing a handful of Wrens. They made their escape through the swing doors. Archie had been hot on their heels but heard their clatter of feet on the balcony steps, so discreetly retreated. He had a much better plan! He turned back to the swimming pool and saw Ted still fumbling about in the water nearby. Archie looked around and retrieved a large, galvanised bucket hanging by the doors. Shouting, Archie enquired, "Do you want this bucket Ted?" Having heard the giggles above him, Ted nodded then made one long, elongated move within the pool – grabbing the bucket from Archie, he swooped water from the surface and flung it upwards to the balcony.

Realising some of the implications, the Commander lent forward in his attempt to stand up from his seated position, as he looked over the balcony 'hoping against all hope'. Two gallons of chlorinated water hit him full on. Archie, at the water's edge now, realised what had happened. Being somewhat of an actor, class comedian and clown he fell backwards in mock horror, saluting as he landed in the pool, and then enquired as he emerged, "Pack my kit for China Sir?" Ted discreetly followed Archie's mock guilt theme, kept his head down, dropped the bucket into the water,

Naval Terms Illustrated – "Hands to Bathe"

climbed slowly out of the pool and disappeared under the balcony – out of sight and hopefully out of mind.

The Wrens rushed over to the Commander in an attempt to soothe and calm his fevered and wet brow. Some moments passed before Snape realised that he wasn't angry anymore, luckily for Pat and Ted who had escaped to the locker room.

Ode to Spring

Spring is here – I've heard it said,
Three deep breaths – leap out of bed.
Land in snow – ankle deep,
Leap back in – and go to sleep.

Ode to the Birds in Spring

The spring is sprung – the grass is ris –
I know where the birdies is.
They've gone to town for Jolly Jack –
I hope they're *'intacta'* when they come back.

Hard Layers

Girls are made to love and kiss –
in my youth an ancient matelot told me this.
He sailed the world in many climes –
and told me of his real hard times.

Pompey once came top of his list –
but nowadays his chance is missed.
Commercial Road, Guildhall Square, his stamping ground –
many a buxom blonde he found.

"J/Sig Bloggs Sir – requests permission to keep a pet on board!"

For Plymouth – he was also keen –
parade the Hoe or Union Street scene.
Cast his net and cast it wide –
end with redhead at his side.

Chatham, the Medway and all that ilk –
their beer went down as smooth as silk.
Girls will be girls – they've clicked at last –
with him they'd end with murky past.

Up the Thames to London Town –
no more time to dance and clown.
The London dolly – so smooth and sleek –
kept him occupied – all the week.

Rosyth to Edinburgh – and down Leith Walk –
find a girl to chat and talk.
Go to hostelry for 'stirrup cup' –
invited home – 'saddle up'.

Gibraltar's Rock – so tall and steep –
face at lace curtains – just a peep.
Follow the offer – for a little while –
return to ship – with a crafty smile.

Algiers, the Kasbah – establishment Black Cat –
women and wine – and things like that.
Waitresses all had graces and airs –
drink your 'plonk' – get your change upstairs.

Malta, that isle – so clear and sunny –
the Valletta 'Gut' girls – all charms and honey.
Beer and big eats – for his runs ashore –
traps a bird – and makes a score.

Alexandria in Egypt and Sister Street –
watch out where you direct your feet.
Sporting Club – swimming bath – all that talent –
proved that he was suave and gallant.

Date palms – desert dunes – the 'Sphinx' tented Camp –
sand bags, concrete paths, lighted oil lamp.
Now he just has one more wish –
to spend another night with his 'bint' – in Sidi Bishr.

"We can take an occasional cut-throat or murderer,
but … definitely *no sailors!*"

Massawa in the Red Sea – stinking hot –
three weeks each month – that's your lot.
A week in the hills – each month to recoup –
a couple more dollies – he was able to scoop.

That's far from the end of this Jolly Tar –
now he's down at Zanzibar.
The slave trade isle – a trade that was vile –
he claims another dolly – in just a while.

In Durban – as a matelot of some resource –
he often visited their race course.
Many a filly – so frivolous and fine –
helped him have – a grand old time.

Cape Town – Adelaide Street – District Six –
watch it Jack – or police will fix.
Play it quiet – with her slide home –
smirk and grin – whilst messmates moan.

Africa's west or east coast – all the same –
any old port – he'd pursue his game.
Stick his neck out – at any time –
to trap his maidens – in tropical clime.

Sri Lanka he knew as old Ceylon –
he was never one to be put upon.
Greetings, salaams and the eternal curry –
leave girlfriend's bed – in flying hurry.

"I wonder if they ever have bush or grass fires here?"

Singapore Susie – with splendid smile –
held him in check – for just a while.
But when she got – all clinging and coy –
he fobs her off – with another ploy.

Hong Kong girls – with slant eyes, slit skirt –
Eastern methods on how to flirt.
Eyelids fluttering – a lovely habit –
stand well back – let the dog see the rabbit.

Now he is slowing down with age –
turning into – a ripe old sage.
You young sailors – just watch it, Jack –
you'll finish like him – with a poor bad back.

Signs of the Times

Fatima Latimer – a girl of some charms –
Was knocking back gins – in the King's Arms.
Doesn't help beauty, for it to keep pace –
She shall have wrinkles – all over her face.

Ode to Age (1)

Ted of the Med – was great in bed,
Could operate thrice nightly.
Alas, alack – poor old back,
He is seldom now so sprightly.

Draft Chit (3)

by Merry Swan

Immediately following the war, many excellent swimmers and water polo players were leaving the Services. The re-build of swimming potential for competition in the Navy was usually thought of in terms of selection from the seaman's branch. However there was, with some reluctance, an exception made for a wood-butcher and a nut-and-bolt bender who were both beginning to dominate Navy swimming and both held shore posts in Portsmouth. Most waterlogged types would dive into a wet handkerchief, provided it was laid flat, and these two were no exception.

Now tradition had qualifiers scrubbing out the gymnasium after stand easy on a Friday afternoon. Through a set of swing doors from there, the Swimming Bath Staff had no classes so emptied the water from the pool on a Friday afternoon and usually scrubbed out on a Saturday morning.

About this time the Admiralty decided to call Ted in as a Staff Instructor for the Baths at Pitt Street in Portsmouth, probably so they could keep an eye on him. However now Ted had charge of the pool and was left to his own resources on Friday afternoons. He was reluctant to empty the pool hastily because there was an amalgamation of swimming talents, Jack the carpenter and Harry the engineer being included. In fact, there was never any need to summon Harry, as he could always be found gravitating from the barracks towards the boiler house every Friday afternoon. He usually held a piece of oily waste in his hand, ready to check all the lumps of coal but always managed to get into the Bath with the Staff and a water polo ball.

"Pass it here Harry!" Ted shouted as he belted down the pool towards the shallow end. Just beyond Frank and John, Harry slammed a skid shot just ahead of Ted. At that precise moment the swing doors opened and there

"Which of you is the boxing and which is the cross-country training group?"

stood Captain Brown, a veritable name in PT circles. He was in full number one uniform, sword and medals included, just popping his head in on the way to help judge at a Court Martial nearby. A gallon of water from Harry's shot formed a perfect parabolic curve, landing straight at the bemeddled chest of Captain Brown. Everyone froze to the position of attention, fingers straight, as technicolour effects crept over the captain's countenance. The silence was broken with, "That was a blood-red silly thing to do. Who is that man?" One of the Instructors quaking at the side of the pool managed to find a voice, "ERA Smith Sir." Away went the DPTS to change his clothes. Harry Smith enquired, "Who was that?" Ted and the others were gob-smacked at Harry's question. He was duly enlightened and informed, "Only Captain Brown, *the* director of PT. You are bound to be in for it now."

The water polo game recommenced. However about five minutes later the ChERA from barracks arrived at the Bath side and called over to Harry, "Get dressed Harry, you're on draft to Theseus in the Far East." Harry's look of astonishment needed to be seen to be believed. He gasped for breath and turned to Ted, "Christopher, your skipper's a fast worker." Harry didn't realise that there were one or two sniggering faces around him. They knew that the Chief Engineer had been chasing Harry for over an hour!

Letter "J" (Jankers, Jail-bait and Jollification)

J is for the jellyfish – it wobbles through the water,
It gets amongst the bathing belles – doing things it didn't oughta.
It lands on arms or back or legs, or sometimes on a torso,
A fish that's far from popular – its sting is even more so.
Should you be stung by this poor fish – whilst swimming in the water,
Try to find yourself a nurse – perhaps someone's blonde daughter.
Apply a balm – wrapped up in charm – and soon you'll feel much better,
Provided you're no Jonah – you should then approve this letter.

"Curses – Foiled!"

A Quiet (gym shoe) Run or Two –
Did it happen to you?

Linda Lovelace Lillington – a girl of some renown –
lived in a house of ill repute – in dear old Pompey town.
Bootnecks by the dozen – matelots by the score –
were often seen quite late at night – knocking on her door.

Matelots when they come ashore – are keen to see bright lights –
often go to dance halls – to fill up boring nights.
Also loaded up with beer – as most of them all drink –
cast envious eyes at dancing girls – as round the floor they slink.

Linda, like a lot of them – was seen in dance halls there –
gin and tonic in one hand – she draped across her chair –
Weighing up the matelots – picking out the prime –
to get to know her really well – they'd all queue up in line.

Matelots often start a fight – over any dolly-bird –
mouthing quite a string of oaths – some you've never heard.
Next of course Patrol arrives – to settle up dispute –
Jack will have a go at them – he doesn't give a hoot.

Eventually he gets hauled off – and taken to the cells –
Sentry, Crusher, OOW – impervious to his yells.
Has a chance to sleep it off – on bench or bunk quite bare –
single blanket, bucket slops – not even simple chair.

Morning after dawns at last – mouth is like a cesspit –
wash and shave – rinse his mouth – tries to disinfect it.
Up on deck – in blazing sun – doesn't help the head –
feeling frazzled round the edges – wishes he was in bed.

Doffs his cap when he sees the Bloke – and listens to the charge –
seems that he's committed crimes – against the world at large.
One, two, three and even more – are trotted out at length –
listens to them reeling off – and prays "Just give me strength".

FO'ARD.

AFT.

Warrant then for badge and rate – as you would expect –
draft chit to accompany it – as kit and hammock checked.
Shift to new horizons – and pastures new and grim –
seems he's not too bad at all – as messmates welcome him.

New ship and new commission – go easy on the beer –
keep to time – toe the line – "You can't do that there 'ere".
His pastures new are foreign – he ploughs around the Med –
sample wines in foreign climes – resolutions leave his head.

Once again – he'll feel no pain – with wine in sense has flown –
So he's up once more before the Bloke – another GC badge is blown.
Later in that commission – he retrieves a badge and rate –
quickly drafted out of ship – after skipper's long debate.

Naval Terms Illustrated - "Hold Water"

And so return to British shores – in quite deflated state –
barrack room mess and runs ashore – in dear old Pompey – mate.
Finds himself on dance hall rounds – as in days gone past –
and like Ulysses of Greek hero fame – needs tying to the mast.

Linda still is queening it – in dance hall near the docks –
would have thought his escapades – made him pull up his socks.
She spots him at the dance hall length and gives out loud cheer –
her prodigal son – her truest one – her cardboard cutout cavalier.

Now its happening all again with his lady of the night –
and once more he feels no pain – as he proceeds to get quite tight.
Is he still wet between the ears? Those lessons – has he learned?
With the passage of his years – how many fingers has he burned?

Hay Burners Ahoy (2)
by Merry Swan

Following Ted's encounter with horses before World War II, his next experience with them was after the war. Ted was selected to represent the Royal Navy in the GB Pentathlon Championships, which partially involved riding a horse.

Now some training was required, although Ted's sense of balance and survival, along with his vast equestrian experiences, lent well in Ted's world. He was surviving admirably over the arena during practise, and was full of confidence when Joe approached him and said, "Well Ted, I know your swimming and fencing skills are strong, but I thought you said you had ridden a horse before. If you don't buck up I will have to put you in the lunge circle and start you off from the very beginning." Ted was offended by this remark. He knew that Joe only came to help with the show jumping a week before. He hadn't had time to get to know the riders or the horses. Ted's mount was having a bit of a lazy day, and he thought he would allow it some slow time. Ted quickly swapped his negatives for positive thoughts. "Joe was right about my strengths. No one here has beaten me at the 200 metres free style swim. As for my epee, I've been doing very well there too. Probably won nine out of each ten points scored." Ted lead the horse round over the dozen jumps one last time before handing him back to the stable boy. He then went over to the pistol shooting range for some practise before tea.

A week of hard graft, practise and a sore backside culminated in the championships. The competition began. Ted excelled at the swimming, he managed to regain some of his wind after the 3000 metres run, his shooting was as well as to be expected, the fencing provided many more points for him, and then came the show jumping.

As 'the team' approached number four, the sheep pen jump, the hay burner thought it was a straight in and out. Unfortunately the rules for this jump were such that the coxswain was meant to execute a 90-degree turn to starboard, in the middle of the pen. Realising the horse was on an incorrect heading, Ted quickly hauled the sharp end round with the head rope, pushed the blunt end round with his heel, came onto the new course and rang down two bells to the engine room for a jump. The engine room misinterpreted its orders, thought it had been three bells, and stopped. Not impressed, Ted decided to heel the horse with his spurs. Not impressed, the hay burner decided to take off.

For the next five minutes Ted managed to hang on for grim death, the reins and the saddle as the horse flew over the water jump – not a splash, cleared the five-bar gate – without a wobble, through the garden path – not a hoof wrong, cleared two doubles and two single jumps and finished on the Irish Bank with another clear and a probable cheesy smile on the horse's face.

So much for Ted's encounter with a hay burner this time, perhaps next time he would have more enjoyment and more control.

"Are you *sure* the altimeter was checked?'

"Hey – you dropped a stitch"

Musings round the Med

Breathes there a matelot – with soul so dead –
Who hasn't served in the sunny Med?
Ploughing through that turquoise sea –
that's where all your dreams should be.

Start at Gibraltar – so tall and steep –
maybe this – is your first peep.
Tricolour, Trianon – Red, White and Blue –
do all these names mean much to you?

Palma in Majorca – and the yacht club there –
bring your own bank manager – put him 'in the chair'.
Very nice island – you've got to admire –
but win Football Pools – before you retire.

Stern to the wall – in old Algiers –
bargaining in the market – will bring you close to tears.
Steps down to the docks – could be fatal too –
if you're weaving back aboard – without a clue.

Marsala of course for those sweet white wines –
is that what he calls – real hard times?
Not too many glasses – you'll get fuzzy in the head –
but then it could happen – almost anywhere in the Med.

Bone was used – for stores galore –
when we convoyed 1st Army supplies during the war.
Hockey, rugby, and football pitches made –
mad scrambles aboard – to repel an air raid.

"Not that one – it's wings are flapping"

Malta standing out – like a festering thumb –
was a stumbling block to the greedy Hun.
History in the making – raiders by the score –
some were the Phoenicians – on that sunlit shore.

Alexandria soon – on the desert's edge –
just as well – you've not 'taken the pledge'.
Raz-el-Tin, Sister Street, Mohammed Ali Square –
steer a 'steady stagger' whenever you are there.

Trucks and buses for the desert runs –
see the shattered tanks, the mines, and the long-range guns.
Very clever lad – he's done it again –
sometime *afterwards* – he visits El Alamein.

"Pilot, are you *sure* this is a shortcut round?"

Cairo then – for just a few days –
the clamour and clutter – has your head in a daze.
The Pyramids, the Sphinx – those Gizeh sights –
the Blue Mosque shining – in the evening lights.

The Suez Canal – for a straight run through –
earth's horizon 'disappears' from view.
Ismalia – for a short sharp stay –
then on through the Lakes – another day.

Sicily and Italy – watch Vesuvius erupt –
North Africa, Sardinia – will he never give up?
Not for him another chance – to do it all again –
his cash will barely stretch – to short holiday in Spain!

"Hey Tubby – she's got a list-a-starboard!"

Ted On The Traps

by Merry Swan

Ted's introduction to the trapeze was at a naval school in the wilds of Suffolk, before the war. He became quite proficient at the back catch and could almost guarantee a one in four success ratio. Being very keen on anything to do with water, it helped Ted that conveniently the trapeze was always located over the Swimming Bath. This bore fruit years later when he was a Staff Instructor for the Royal Navy in Portsmouth, teaching all and sundry trapeze work.

"Fair's fair – can you do this?"

There was to be another rehash of the PT syllabus and Ted was required to assist in the changes. He took the opportunity to work on the trapeze section and introduce the back catch to the syllabus. It hadn't been included up until then and being a move he remembered from way back in time he thought its inclusion might enhance his junior officer status. From the archives of Ted's memory he recalled that it should be something like 'a circle second, a swing through over the second platform, a beat upstart action swinging forward and back; on the return swing, a reach back and catch the first trap backwards then a return to the shallow end platform'. * So the back catch became part of the new syllabus and Ted didn't need to think anymore about it.

*OK, for those laymen here image a platform above either end of the swimming pool with two trapeze bars hanging down like swings, a little way out above each platform, way up high. By sitting on the first bar you swing out from the platform and over the pool to the second platform – 'beat upstart' just being the movement of the legs forward and back to gain a swinging momentum. So, by swinging out a couple of times from the first platform, you then straighten your legs out to catch the second trapeze bar with your knees. Then in one movement you move yourself over to the second bar, but keep the momentum going! Then a couple of swings over the second platform, ready to reach back and catch the first trapeze bar with your hands and land delicately feet first onto the first platform – or not!

Ted used to have a quiet practise on the traps from time to time but found that once he made his commission he was conducting a great number of all practical physical training exams, with no time for himself.

Then came the time for Ted's examination of his first lot of four budding Bosuns on the trapeze. "OK you lovely lot, I want to see ten trapeze moves from the syllabus. You only have one choice. I will select the other nine moves. PTI English is here to observe, see fair play and probably keep his beady eye on me." The budding Bosuns began their exhibition tricks as Ted called out each move. "Move number six. I want to see a back catch, number 22 on the syllabus." The men staggered slightly and looked in amazement. Sam piped up, "We don't know it Sir". Ted gave a quick rendition of the expectations and movements. 'Swing, circle, throw-catch, swing through, beat back, reach backward' … 'splash'. They all had a go and were marked accordingly.

On completion of the remainder of their exam Ted enquired, "Any questions?" "One man piped up, "Yes Sir, how do you do a back catch Sir?" Ted replied, "Trapeze Instructor English will demonstrate a back catch." "Permission to change into trunks Sir?" English was thinking he might get out of it, as the other men tittered. Ted snarled, "Yes, two minutes – full speed." On PTI English's return, he climbed up to the shallow end platform over the pool, waited for the order to go, then began his demonstration – 'swing, circle, throw-catch, swing through, beat back, reach backward …*splash*'. Almost in unison the Bosun bath stewards spoke. "We still haven't seen a back catch Sir."

"The men had worked hard to reach the end of their course." Ted thought to himself. He decided to give them a giggle and show them one of their officers going for a splash. So standing there in an immaculate singlet, sweater, white flannels and spotless gym shoes with ironed laces Ted handed his clipboard, with syllabus and marks, over to English. Ted was ready and expecting a wet-shirt as he climbed up to the platform. So he began … 'Swing, circle, throw-catch, swing through, beat back, reach backward and … *catch it*', then back to the shallow end platform. With a nonchalant wave Ted said, "That gentlemen, was a back catch." There was an unexpected round of applause.

Ted never revealed that it had been over five years since he last attempted that and that it was only by the grace of God and some pure bull, he made it.

"Quickly Commander, have all the men piped off the upper deck!"

Wishful Thinking

Oh to be in Temeraire –
now PT Wrens are everywhere.
Lovely smiling, dimpled face –
I wonder if I could now keep pace?

PT Wrens appear in dreams –
'Target for Tonight' it seems.
If I approach them with a smile –
do you think they – would run a mile?

Grace and style whilst in the gym –
stone-faced instructor has to grin.
Muscles where they never knew –
wasn't it the same with you?

Trim and ship-shape – Bristol style –
will step ashore in just a while.
Dress was never near so shocking –
as 'Nora Batty' wrinkled stocking.

Out they go through gymnasium door –
smart and pert when they step ashore.
Watch it girl – young Clubs may follow –
will they look as smart on their return tomorrow?

Frayed and frazzled – they start again –
next morning – in the pouring rain.
Round and round the track they'll go –
to show how tough – they'll do it in snow.

Staff Instructors sing and shout –
whilst dainty damsels dance about.
IF ONLY… but that could never be –
they wouldn't trust a 'skate' like me.

Naval Terms Illustrated – "Deadlight"

Sparring partner – 'Get stripped – you're on next'

In days of old – when knights were bold,
Many a tale of frustration told.
When rushing to his true love's bed,
Two hours work – with spanner instead.

Ode to Display Teams

In display teams – like heavenly stars,
'Clubs' swing around their parallel bars.
Years advance – and like a clown,
Can't even now – stand upside down.

An Ode or Three – to the PT Wrens – From Me

Now that Wrens have qualified –
they wear a PT badge with pride.
We vintage thought we were the best –
should we tear the badge from off our chest?

We old time stars had been denied –
sights that would have satisfied.
Not for us a chance to see –
shapely leg and dimpled knee.

"Don't fence epée with the Wrens – Yer Point d'Arrêt 'll drop off!"

Hairy chest and sweaty sock –
was our Monday morning shock.
Ego shattering visual freaks –
with us amongst them – were our treats.

Fencing should have been quite nice –
with this sport – there's not much vice.
Unless it's sabre – the worst of all –
shake your head – see if it falls.

Hurling round the parallel bars –
taking tumbles – seeing stars.
'Volunteer' males to apply a balm –
on leg or thigh (especially) or dainty arm.

Bandage and band-aid – soon apply –
knowing nudge – and winking eye.
Were they all of stony face –
or, with address and phone book each keep pace?

How about the boxing – girls?
did you wear headscarves – to hide your curls?
Jimmy Wilde's wife used to spar with him –
did the males volunteer again in the gym?

In and out of swimming bath –
surely traps were quite a laugh.
Built-in cups for duck suit top –
protection from a 'splash' or knock.

Floor work next – with some panache –
fronts and backs – give them all a bash.
Each accomplished with great ease –
unless of course – you have duck's disease?

Never mind the bookwork – striving –
did they teach the art of skiving?
Or were you thrown in – at the 'deep-end' –
skip-jump, press-ups, full knee bend?

High box – did you have a go?
or dance and movement – quick, quick, slow?
Stepladders can be drawn from Stores?
for high box – did you apply for yours?

Physiology, anatomy and all that stuff –
medical lectures can be tough.
But the main question – really is whether –
you put the whole of 'Oscar' (the model) together?

Rugby refs are always wanted –
were you girls – still undaunted?
Qualify, yes – but don't go daft –
especially in the communal bath.

To make sure they're all – on the right tack –
spike shoe work on field and track.
Stamina training in this – I bet'cha –
to escape the clutching hand of lecher.

Then again they may be keen –
with 'lecher' clubswinger to be seen.
Modern 'clubs' just cannot be –
Travolta type of 'clubs' – like me.

Should they not – all take a bow –
these girls have really qualified now.
But will these new 'quals' now go to sea –
as the waves aren't as big as they used to be?

"Oh no … it's *much* too rough!"

Pensioners Yardarm Clearance Chit

Not me Chief Wren – I do not smoke –
It must have been another bloke.
Nobody loves me now I'm old and grey –
I didn't put that Wren – in the family way.

Memorable Malta

Malta in the sunny Med – it will always be –
a haven to the sailor – from his life at sea.
Rocks upon the seashore – clear and sunny clime –
give yourself a run ashore – get back on board on time.

Wartime introduction to the 'pivot' of the Med –
not entirely happy – just as well that I'm not wed.
Ploughing the Atlantic – pushing south at speed –
leading in the Squadron – stragglers take heed.

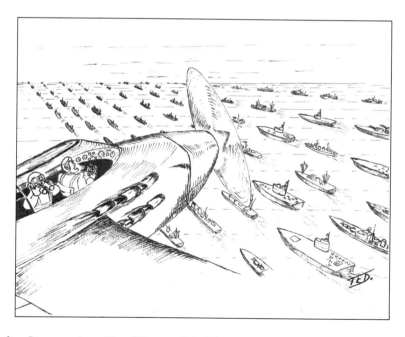

Malta Convoy Aug 42 – "He wouldn't be so damned pleased about 'mare
nostrum' if he had my job of picking out our ship in this lot!"

Key of the Mediterranean – slide through after dark –
gather up the convoy – careful … U boat 'shark'.
Shepherd them together – "Lead off No.1" –
"Close up in your columns – this one won't be fun".

Go on Malta Convoy – do 'Ohio' run –
watch Italian bombers – converging from the sun.
From the Balearics onward – Jerry presses the attack –
at last – you thank your lucky stars – you are coming back.

Biplanes, creaking Gladiators – flying through the air –
named Faith, Hope and Charity – they defended there.
Diving, twisting, turning – those beautiful Three Graces –
what a treat to see a smile – on the locals' faces.

"**?! (censored) … aircraft ovar thar!"

118

Then it's some years later – return to Malta's clime –
just enjoy this little stay – make most of it this time.
On those Shore Establishments – duties here and there –
plenty time for runs ashore – but check on 'wear and tear'.

Ships are always moving – up and down the trot –
steer well clear of all of them – or it'll be your lot.
Motorboat and Skimmer – with their creaming wake –
Cox'n keep a sharp look out – can't afford mistake.

Halyards snapping signals – up and down the mast –
semaphore and signalling – thought they're in the past.
Flashing light on yardarm – calling up the base –
a knowledge of these signals – you can then keep pace.

"No lad – it wasn't a low flying aircraft!"

Banyans out to Gozo – picnics on the shore –
children by the boatload – screaming out for more.
Dghajsa cross the harbour – don't stand up to wave –
otherwise you'll topple – then it's 'Hands to Bathe'.

Football and some hockey – on Corradino Heights –
the canteen after football – on balmy Maltese nights.
Shiver when the sun goes down – in jersey, cap and shorts –
warm it up by drinking beer – and then a coupla snorts.

Up to the Barraca – to watch the ships come in –
then Hotel Phoenicia – to drink a large pink gin.
Perhaps there is a dance on – so toddle in and see –
only 'Mother's Union' – not quite my cup of tea.

Trips up to Valletta – stagger down 'the Gut' –
stir up tons of trouble – defaulters then – all but.
Drinking pints of warmish beer – a bottle of Ambeet –
weaving back on board next morn – feels I've two left feet.

"Huh – Following wind – no spinnaker!"

Florianna Floozie – and very Frivolous Fred –
never get enticed by them – to rest your weary head.
Far too dodgy customers – extremely dubious past –
don't let on to shipmates – aspersions they will cast.

Beer, big eats and dance halls – are beckoning tonight –
down the 'Steps to Ruin' – "Are you spoiling for a fight?"
A floor show's on at Minco's – may as well look in –
there, find dancing partner – another double gin.

And as the rake makes progress – whilst stationed on the isle –
perhaps he's learnt a thing or three – and smirks a crafty smile.
So he thinks he's 'made it' – is wise beyond his years.
Even more important – Has he grown up between the ears?

Ships go out on exercise – submarines and that –
creeping in past midnight – black as father's hat.
Swishing of the bow-wave – 'Piping of the still'.
Am I too nostalgic?.. Forget?.. I never will.

Ode to Twinkle Toes (1)

With young dolly – in disco dance –
Show her how to skip and prance.
Then country stroll – a healthy lass –
Administer – a *'coup de grass'*.

Ode to Twinkle Toes (2)

Way back in time – he shot a line,
About prowess at dancing.
Now you won't see – him bend a knee,
Old age has stopped him prancing.

A Block Off The Old Chip

by Merry Swan

In the last few years of an undistinguished career Ted managed to scrape a commission, despite varying fortunes over a long period in the Royal Navy. Once he had settled himself to a steady stagger, he persuaded a luckless female to marry him and bear his children. As a Physical Training Officer Ted was involved in the social life on camp. This was due to the fact that the gymnasia in the land Establishments were used for a variety of functions including dances, plays, concerts, church and even physical training. Thus it was that the wardroom Christmas children's party would be held at the gymnasium in Ted's establishment.

"Come on you lot. We need to get this laid up tonight. The little cherubs will be arriving on the dot tomorrow – not late, like you layabouts". Ted barked out instructions while he was up a ladder struggling with the brushwork to a shark's head, as the seaweed he had just painted obscured it. He was excited with his efforts of a treasure chest and the other mural of a parrot in the 'little' corner. He realised that the crepe streamers and paper chains still hadn't been put up and was about to give out further earfuls of abuse when Barber approached him. "Sir, will you be much longer with the ladder. Only we still have to put the decorations up for the ceiling". There were some large fishing nets, glass floats and lanterns lying on a table nearby. "Use a table Barber, get Thomson to help. But don't you go breaking your neck or the Chief will have my guts for garters – and while you're at it get those streamers and chains up somewhere". There were a variety of skull and crossbones' party hats now laid out at each setting, and cardboard swords and eye patches on a separate table for those who would want one. In the 'little' corner near the entrance a sailor was setting a table out with a black cloth, a pot of red ink and a stamp pad. The gymnasium was beginning to transform into a veritable pirate's cave.

Whispering to his wife, Ted said "You'll have to bring the boys in a while. I must check that everything is ready". He opened the front door to leave. Nicholas heard the door and scrabbling down the stairs shouted "Daddy, Daddy we'll be late for the party if you go out now!" "If I'm not back in time, Mummy will take you boys". There were now three anxious-looking faces peering through the balustrades at him. "Now finish getting changed and don't forget your Ps and Qs. The Commander will be there". Ted made a fast exit and rushed over to the gymnasium.

As he arrived he was greeted with a comical scene. Barber and Thomson were wrestling with what looked to be a very drunken sailor dressed all in black with a goldfish bowl on his head. "You fools! Even I can see from here what the problem is". Ted lunged forward in aid as Barber swung round attempting to acknowledge Ted's presence but unable to. Their heads cracked together. "Blithering idiot!" was all Ted could summon up as he grabbed the side of his head in pain. "S..Sorry Sir, my fault entirely Sir". For a split second Ted wished he was back at home with three very over-excited boys of his own. Thomson attempted to relieve the tense situation. "Christmas tree is in place and fully decorated Sir, everything's ship-shape". "Except Jack here", Ted was pointing at the much deflated Jack. Ted left Thomson to deal with Jack as Barber held on and rubbed his aching head.

The silence inside the pirate's cave was eerie. But at the far end of the gym there was a large, quiet shout from the lights on the tree and the brightly coloured presents underneath. More importantly, the senior officers dressed as pirates, would have to acknowledge Ted's genius. There was to be a strict order of service from the pirates and a quick change of costume by the Commander. However, before any of that, Ted needed to coerce and cajole the willing and unwilling children into the cave. That was where Jack came into his own.

Ted fed witticisms to Thomson, who was now in full control of the re-inflated 'Jack', an empty dive suit with the fish bowl now replaced by a football, painted with a face and moustache, and forming an airtight seal at the neck line. The 'diver' greeted and welcomed the children as they arrived. There was a "Ho, ho, ho and a gottle of geer" from the side, if the Mum was especially pretty. While still in the 'little' corner, the children were required to sign their own certificate of allegiance to the pirates in blood with their own thumbprint. They were then to be stamped on the forearm with the pirate's mark. Ted's three little angels arrived with squeals of joy at the sight of 'Jack'. "Ooh, is this real blood Daddy?" Ian asked enthusiastically as his thumb was plunged onto the red stamp pad. Simon wasn't sure and waited for an answer before he offered his hand forward. Nicholas gave Simon's arm a shove and shouted, "Of course it is. This is a proper pirate's cave, with proper pirates who have proper swords and proper blood!"

Once the children were allowed to enter the cave, they queued as quietly as possible by the tree as they all watched the arrival of Father Christmas. Each child was then given a present and time to enthuse over them before they were ushered to the tables ready for the food. This gave the Commander time to change from Santa into chief pirate. A complete demolition job was steadfastly executed on the mountains of trifles, jellies, jam tarts, mince pies, sausage rolls and even the sandwiches. The children eagerly awaited the ceremony of cutting the cake by the chief pirate, with a naval sword. The pirates then circulated the table offering cake to each of the children. The chief pirate (and Commander) arrived beside Nicholas, Ted's number one son. "Nicholas, would you like a little piece of cake?" With a forthright reply came "No thank you, I'd rather have a big piece".

Ted wasn't sure whether to salute his son with both hands, pat him on the back or give him a gold medal for telling the Commander the truth; or to disown him and investigate the milkman's activities some years earlier!

Safety at Work

Milkman coming down garden path –
Give kids on lawn – an almighty laugh.
Place foot on skate – a contorted face –
Crate, milk, glass – all over the place.

"Look me straight in the eye… and tell me, who gave you the horseshoes?"

Tales of Ted's Travels
or
A Pensioners Plea – for a Wren on his Knee

Being wet behind the ears –
is the curse of our youthful years.
As the years advance – they say –
charm, wit, wisdom – come our way.

I wonder where I have gone wrong? –
certainly this – is not my song.
Brawn and brain – just never mix –
old dogs never learn new tricks.

Into battle – I'd often wade –
to 'pull' a buxom blonde barmaid.
Sometimes come off second best –
massive boyfriends – do not jest.

Then again – the dice may fall –
right way up – no sweat at all.
Problem then – was to be found –
return on board – all safe and sound.

Once or twice I'd miss the boat –
find myself – before the Bloke.
Involved excuses – never helped –
often came away – well scalped.

Dreams and the dreamer (2)

Bushy eyebrows – wrinkled gaze –
always peering through a haze.
"Stream the fog buoy – it'll do no harm" –
"Not too close" – or – "Buy a farm".

Badges come – and badges go –
on his 'taut' ship – a constant flow.
Badge restored – then once more –
every six months – a run ashore.

Pattern seldom ever changed –
Commander often felt deranged.
Sometimes swore – and tore his hair –
frayed out with the whole affair.

"Musso remembers an urgent date!"

Once he caught me on the hop –
restored a badge – quick draft, full stop.
Exiled in Egypt – desert sand –
tented Camp – at least on land.

Mend your ways – bear up and smile –
things get better – in a while.
Blue seas, date palms, runs ashore –
your luck has changed – do you want more?

Another 'clubs' (Joe) at DQ's – Raz-el-Tin –
sometimes went ashore with him.
Not much help – my murky past –
often bubbled up – real fast.

"Oh no Sir, I was nowhere near the Kasbah."

Alexandria for these runs ashore –
but don't go daft – as you did before.
Cairo came up – once or twice –
sojourn there – overall quite nice.

Shufti bint – in yashmak fair –
curvy shape – and henna hair.
Kasbah cuties – sloe-eyed charm –
"watch it Clubs – you'll come to harm".

Onion beer – sometimes quite nice –
provided drunk – with tons of ice.
But local wine – has quite a kick –
leave well alone – p..p..p..push off – real quick.

Escapades there – by the score –
on Egypt's hot and sandy shore.
Back to Camp – in 'fragile' state –
still regarded – as a skate.

Mosquito net lifted – torch on bed, alight –
always attracts them – late at night.
Clubs weaves to tent – falls into bed –
awakes with bites – sore throat, thick head.

Times soon change – they always say –
come back home – one wintry day.
Murky past will never mention –
soldier on – and take a pension.

To turn a phrase – I've always heard –
is an easy way – to 'pull' a bird.
But 'O' in English – not in woodwork –
hence my efforts – never could work.

"Sit down sir – and I'll put you in a trance!"

I never make a 'hit' somehow –
barmaids all wear spike shoes now.
They quickly exit – from my scene –
as fleet of foot – I've never been.

Bints and barmaids have had to go –
now I creep about – real slow.
Crafty Clubs – now looks again –
for the days – when it comes on to rain.

Now PT Wrens – my maidens fair –
why not choose me? Grey beard – no hair.
Good looks of course – you'll see beneath –
shortly now though – minus teeth.

But these fit young girls – may not be keen –
with Ancient Mariner – to be seen.
Now all these yarns – of course, are true –
Would I ever lie to you?

Hands To Bathe

by Merry Swan

Through some strokes of good luck, Ted was promoted to the exalted rank of Bosun for the last few years of his naval career. An appointment was offered for Ted to join the Staff of Commander-in-Chief, Mediterranean in Malta. He also found himself jockeyed into the Flag Officer, Malta's Staff, thus wearing two Staff caps.

"Hey look ... sixth from the right, fifth row – he's got swastikas on him!"

Ultimately Ted was invited to join the retinue of Staff Officers accompanying FOM on Admiral's rounds. This would be a first for Ted. "Being 22nd in the parade behind the Admiral is better than being the one to 'kick the ship's cat'" Ted mused to himself. These were not quite the same as Captain's rounds and could certainly be classed as very official. They only happened once in a blue moon. The Admiral and his good lady had invited two junior officers and their wives to join in a buffet luncheon at the Admiral's villa across the harbour, Ted being one of them. Ted found the invite most acceptable and it softened the blow from feeling like one or two up from the ship's cat in importance. "Fay will be pleased. This will mean she *has* to have a new frock! The prospects of hobnobbing with the Admiral's wife will excite her enormously."

After rounds his barge landed the Admiral home then set off for the opposite side of the harbour to collect Ted and his wife at the Customs House steps. Still in best uniform, minus medals and sword, Ted motored down to Customs House and parked up. There was going to be gold braid everywhere and Ted hoped he looked smart, as he adjusted his tie for the third time. "I'm glad I decided on a suit for today. It's a little breezy and will be worse out on the harbour", Fay announced as she carefully stepped out of the car, clutching her bag and gloves. Ted was busying himself looking out for the Admiral's barge, but had noticed the Grand Harbour rippling a bit. It was coming into Gregale season but no orders had been given that day for ship's boats to use the more sheltered steps nearby, so Ted paid no more thought to the ripples as their lift approached. Crossing the harbour and safely arriving at the villa's jetty, Ted chivalrously aided his dear wife from the boat with a supporting hand and spare arm, thanked the coxswain and escorted Fay up to the big house. They were politely greeted and immediately put at ease by the Admiral and his wife with a quiet, relaxing glass of sherry.

Pleasant conversation was exchanged throughout luncheon, the four guests participating of good food and a glass of wine to aid digestion. Then there came the thought of 'back to work' for the two junior officers. So farewells were exchanged and Ted and Fay proceeded down to the villa's jetty ready for the return journey to the Valletta side of the harbour. Ted had noticed that during the lunchtime break the water's surface seemed to have turned from a bit of a ripple to a lop. They embarked the boat, which then made a rather lumpy journey back. The lop was definitely increasing in height and depth. By the time they arrived at their destination Ted knew his previous polite gestures of helping hand and arm for his wife would have to be much more distinctive and gentlemanly. As they came alongside, Ted rose to the sea's challenge and the barge's rise and fall. He firmly placed one foot on the steps and one foot on the boat's gunwale. Then he grasped Fay firmly by her forearm and opposite elbow. Ted issued the order, "Step out – quickly when I tell you". Now as a good first lieutenant, Ted's wife obeyed all orders and stepped when directed.

Freeze-frame and envisage the situation. One tailored ladies' suit with tight-fitting skirt, one hat with small veil, a clutch bag, pair of gloves and a pair of stiletto-heeled shoes – the perfect ensemble for any lady on a luncheon date. Unfortunately Fay's foot didn't make it to the steps. As if to compensate, she let out a high-pitched squeal, swung round towards Ted and grabbed at his shoulder just as the boat sheered away. This put Ted in a precarious position of the splits and almost ruined his married life, especially as his wife fell backwards into Grand Harbour and he could only watch helplessly. Immediately Ted was forced to execute a perfect forward dive, fully booted in best uniform.

As he surfaced he realised there were two priorities to be dealt with. The roll and yaw of the boat's movement, which was likely to spread Ted and his wife, like jam against the stone wall of the steps, and the fact that his wife was a non-swimmer. Tensing himself into an L shape, Ted quickly threw the back of his shoulders against the boat, lunged his feet against the wall, grabbed Fay around the waist, and shouting, ordered the Maltese coxswain to 'bear off' and 'stop engines'.

Fay had slightly different priorities. Maybe she was thinking of Ted's bank balance, but she made some very exaggerated and slashing motions towards various pieces of her apparel. "Where's my other shoe …", "Mind my hat …", "My bag …". Fay began to take in water. She had forgotten she could not swim. From his disadvantaged place on the surface, Ted heaved Fay up and towards the boatmen, hoping they could grab her arms as they flailed past them. Ted then ordered the crew to land his wife at the other set of steps, after hauling her aboard. He began to swim away from the heavy wash and the stone wall.

Having followed orders and landed Fay ashore, the crew then, almost in a trance, turned to 'man-overboard' boat drill. The Maltese bowman quickly heaved Ted the heavy, cork lifebelt. Unfortunately this landed squarely on top of Ted's head with sufficient force as to jam his service cap down over his brows and send jets of water out of his ears. In his best gymnasium voice, Ted spoke loudly in smatterings of Arabic, Afrikaans and German leaving the crew in no doubt as to Ted's thoughts on the bowman's parentage. They wisely decided to leave Ted to make his own way back to dry land.

The following day Fay received a visit from the Admiral's wife, who was very concerned and most solicitous about the whole affair. At work, Ted knew the grapevine had been humming and his colleagues believed that Ted and his wife had partaken of more than a glass of wine and one sherry. They were unaware that the Admiral was teetotal. One outcome on the credit side – Ted and his wife were able to dine out on the story a few times.

"Recover Torpedoes/The Return"

Soldier on to the Sexy Sixties

Now those in the Navy can stay till they're sixty –
a matelot could become like a wizened pixie –
And soldiering on into his eighth five –
could appear more dead – than ever alive.

But for Wrens – does this apply? –
their silken hose – and rounded thigh –
Could put you off – unless you too –
are myopic in your ancient view.

With spectacles, gums and leering gaze –
and addled brain in quite a haze –
Head well forward – shoulders bent –
in immaculate suit from rent-a-tent.

"Not that card, it causes a faster pulse rate!"

Walking sticks will return to fashion –
and Ancient Mariner in heat of passion –
Gallops to his true love fair –
trips on his beard of long grey hair.

If like this – you come to grief –
you'll weep into your handkerchief –
Whilst lying prone – in flaked out state –
your Wren absconds with your best mate.

Beard with 'snood' will become the thing –
a lengthening of 'regulation trim' –
But what of the 'pate' – so sparse, so thin –
less fluff than on a baby's chin.

Perhaps the Pusser – will relent –
and like his suits – from rent-a-tent –
Have toupees in the Naval Stores –
when will you – qualify for yours?

Then of course – from days of yore –
what else is in that Naval Store?
Hammock ladders – there might be –
for the old and bold – who go to sea.

Bunks and foam mattress they'll despise –
whilst peering from their rheumy eyes.
With hammock – almost break their neck –
their agility lands them on the deck.

"Chiefy .. it's about time I had some new gym shoes"

Flannel nightshirts again – become the rage –
modelled by some ripe old sage.
Tasselled night cap – all Pussers dress –
candlestick holder – as you can guess.

"Tuck me up dear Sergeant – in my little Army bed" –
this phrase came from the Army – so it has been said.
What about the Jossman – and Regulating Staff –
tucking up each hammock? – their lot will all go daft.

If 'My Lords' in their wisdom – want an Ancient Jack –
do you think that they – will have this old one back?
At my vintage – I'm sure I've missed the boat –
"What was that you said – I'm a silly Old Goat?"

"Fix this Doc – I pruned it rather heavily"

Ode to Income Tax (1)

Standing at the kitchen sink –
Feeling great and in the pink.
Postman's knock – comes at the door –
Income Tax – I'm feeling poor.

Ode to Income Tax (2)

Robin Hood and his Merry Men –
Roamed the Forest of Sherwood then.
Robbing people – is still not lax –
Biggest robbers – income tax.

Ode to the Garage Bill

Whilst coming home from pub – quite late –
Drive my car – straight through the gate.
Like 'chips' – the other side descend –
Radiator, engine block, sump, big end.

Ode to Weather

Whilst watching the snowflakes fall –
I don't like the prospects at all.
Non-starting car – no pub for a 'jar' –
And snow trodden all over the hall.

The Beer Barons Guide to Conservation

If returning home – in evening light –
you leave the car – slam door quite tight.
May as well go for a 'jar' –
keys are locked in 'blood-red' car.

If chased from house – by irate spouse –
take heart – you're not the only louse.
Retire to pub – and gulp down beer –
return after too many – she'll bend your ear.

If herons land upon your lawn –
negative goldfish – ere the dawn.
If however rabbits romp –
appear with gun – old buck will stomp.

If bathing – and playing with rubber duck –
in cold water tap – big toe gets stuck.
Don't just scream and lose your head –
sink whiskies – served by blonde – instead.

If working in the garden shed –
tools – you've loaned next door, to Fred.
Nip down road – for crate of beer –
"Bad growing season this year – dear".

"You go on ahead…"

If over garden wall – Fred does appear –
and calls you out – to drink some beer.
Don't let your missus know about it –
on your return – she'll scream and shout it.

If elephants on your lawn do eat –
not much room for their big feet.
Unless they're pink – from visions clear –
after drinking too much beer.

If cows cavort upon your lawn –
"Pancake Tuesday" – ere the dawn.
If perhaps – they meekly graze –
milk, cream, yoghurt – all your days.

"It's that ginger tom – I spotted him just now!"

If on your lawn – rhinos appear –
it is your duty – to stand well clear.
If engine room – starts to accelerate –
flying leap – right over gate.

If giraffe on lawn – should nibble and graze –
are you sure you're not – in alcoholic haze?
Retire indoors – and knock back gin –
when flaked right out – you'll get rid of him.

If vultures on your lawn descend –
perhaps your ways – you ought to mend.
Stop drinking now – while you've the time –
no beer or whisky – just gin and lime.

"… and this one thought I'd missed …"

If on your lawn – lions rant and roar –
tell it to old Fred – next door.
If he has heard them out there too –
he's been down local pub with you.

If flight of flamingos on lawn appear –
almost as bad as pink elephants here.
Disregard – and do not worry –
return to pub in flying hurry.

If wallabies in your duck pond wallow –
stop your drinking till tomorrow.
Retire to couch – should it be handy –
take half a bottle – medicinal brandy.

If kangaroos on your lawn do crowd –
no use shouting out aloud.
Make sure all your debts are paid –
then drink your whisky – with lemonade.

If laying on floor – in frazzled state –
accused of drunkenness by mate.
You're stone cold sober – not to be put upon –
if lying there without holding on.

The Fifth Year School Leaver

There was once a young lady named Mame –
Who left school – and went on the game.
She hawked her wares – on high-rise block stairs –
And her housemaster helped her to fame.

"It's just given itself a long weekend from Thursday to Tuesday – with an occasional day on Wednesday!"

Ode to Age (3)

Younger than springtime am I
What a load of 'Pie in the Sky'.
Barnacles round my copper-bottom –
Ain't you glad that you ain't got 'em?

Ode to Weather (whether?)

I never go out in the rain...
It soaks right through to my brain.
It makes it go rusty
Stops me feeling lusty –
... I never go out in the rain.

"Geraldine? Geraldine! Is that his change from £5?"

Homo Sapiens

We're political, we're animal, we're sometimes quite mechanical –
but seldom when it's needed on the car.
We're lyrical, satirical and think it quite a miracle –
our repairs have kept it going quite so far.

We're dramatic, emphatic and often quite fanatic –
when arguing a 'point' to make it clear.
We're mendacious, loquacious and frequently pugnacious –
if the 'point' – is paying for a round of beer.

In trepidation, high elation, woman has emancipation –
as the boss she'll tell you what to do.
Equal rights, a boss in tights – or slacks – we often see some sights –
and miles of queues outside a woman's loo.

We're moonful, we're tuneful and romantic by the spoonful –
whilst singing of our true love in the tub.
We're gregarious and precarious, and often quite hilarious –
when stepping on the soap – that is the rub.

We're splendiferous, herbivorous and sometimes quite vociferous –
when taking blonde from office out to dine.
We're commendable and dependable – language can be rendable –
when faced with price list for the cost of wine.

We're audacious, sagacious and frequently flirtatious –
when lining up a 'bird' for run ashore.
We're painless, we're aimless, and often think we're blameless –
when told by bird 'enough' – she wants no more.

Naval Terms Illustrated – "Flying Light"

We're impetuous, we're lecherous, making life quite treacherous –
when caught by wife on phone to fancy 'bint'.
We're accused, bemused and frequently confused –
we can't take her on the town when we are skint.

We're vivacious, sagacious and very much tenacious –
when dating the new barmaid in the pub.
We're dedicated, medicated and probably would be desiccated –
if buxom barmaid wielded heavy club.

Now me of course, I'm different – and think I'm quite omnipotent –
when prancing round and doing daily chores.
My blondes, my barmaids and 'bints' – all take my subtle hints –
they're charming, wise and witty – "Why? – Ain't yours?"

"Beachcombing again, eh? Well you can take *that* back!"

February 14th

Valentine again comes round –
Without a word, without a sound.
Batchelor proud – smiling and gay –
She'll have you name – the wedding day.

Ode to Youth (2)

The days of my youth – were quite uncouth
And choice of girls was random.
In these ripe old years – a few more beers
And seldom now ride tandem.

Going Crackers at Christmas

First it's school that closes – children cheer and shout –
holidays are here again – you know that school is out.
Skateboards, bikes and roller-skates – and chasing round the park –
nothing said dissuades them – from their little lark.

Christmas is upon us – in all its tinselled form –
special foods and special wine – divergence from the norm.
Holidays are holidays – especially when you're young –
energy, imagination and an almost ceaseless tongue.

"Mine has just returned from his Australian tour!"

Town Hall square – with Christmas tree –
decorated, garlanded, as it should be.
Across each street they've strung some more –
decorations – enough to make eyes sore.

Plastic snowflakes – and coloured lights –
leaping reindeer from dizzy heights.
Notices in shop windows hail –
commencement of their January sales.

Shops have each got crackers – cakes and caramels –
mistletoe and holly – and silver burnished bells.
Robins, like Christmas vultures – wheeling overhead –
cardboard cutout candlesticks – on tatty bits of thread.

Wide-eyed in wonder – kids look in shops galore –
up and down the escalator – in and out the door.
Pocket money – sketchy maths – working out their sums –
little present here and there – for family, Dads and Mums.

Kiddies clutching hard Mum's hand –
queue for entrance to Fairyland.
Hope to enter Santa's Cave –
Mum warns – that they must all behave.

Blushing, coy and shy they stand –
in front of Santa in Fairyland.
Tongue-tied – they cannot all just sprout –
coaxed – they eventually get it out.

Dads – with parcels wrapped up tight –
trying to hide them – from kiddies' sight.
Quickly – in car boot with these –
deaf – to any childish pleas.

And then it's journey back home – to friendly warmth and cheer –
Dad's sideboard cupboard topped up – with whisky, wine and beer.
Christmas cards across the room – strung on ribboned line –
"Did you post that lot of ours? – Will they get there in time?"

Christmas Eve finds Dad – pushing bicycles up the stairs –
presents, stockings and parcels – give him a few grey hairs.
Done at last – returns to lounge – with Mum takes glass of wine –
fervently hope – that kids don't wake – at 4 am this time.

At last its Christmas morning – bedroom bedlam reigns –
kids tear open parcels – despite poor Santa's pains.
Hooting, shrieks and shouting – and gallop up and down –
poor parents wish that they – were somewhere else in town.

Piles of shedded needles – from Christmas tree in corner –
angel on the top – smiles down like Jackie Horner.
Offsprings milling round the foot – guessing parcels and which shape –
very largest one of all – is father's *little* jape.

Lunch, with turkey, crackers – perhaps a glass or two –
paper hats from crackers – tin-whistles? – a jaundiced view.
Subside in chair to hear the speech – with children – never could.
Remains? One mince pie, cold custard and soggy Christmas pud.

"Aye! A wee moose"

20th century female

"… and he keeps muttering about rural science and his Form Master, Sir."

Ode to Youth (1)

"Jack Shaloo, one boot one shoe"
I've often heard them say so.
In days of yore that was before
My youth flew out the window.

"It's me pet, Sir – for animal drawing 'O' level."

Ode to the modern dance(rs)

Dizzy, dancing disco dollies,
Sucking sweets and licking lollies.
Music change and with a grin,
Swiftly knock back double gin.

The Office Workers Guide to Living

If dashing down the stairs one morn –
in bedroom slippers old and worn
To answer door – saying – "What the heck" –
don't trip – you'll break your flaming neck.

If travelling on the underground –
with all that noise, the rush, the sound
Bird smiles at you – with some affection –
forget it Jack – you'll miss connection.

If in the office – secretary –
says boss wants you – please be wary
Are you really – hale and hearty? –
what did you call him – at office party?

If office dolly – you take to lunch –
tells you that she has got a hunch
That you are married – just dodge it Jack –
retire to gents – slide out the back.

If Larry Lovelorn – the office lout –
starts to throw his weight about
Arrange a tryst – for him at last –
your wife'll stop – all his bombast.

If talking on the telephone –
to girl who says she'd like to roam
Be careful missus isn't there –
with handbag – she will part your hair.

If sitting down to Sunday lunch –
flowers on table – a lovely bunch
Don't disagree with what wife said –
flowers and vase – will crash on head.

If busty birds – with melon boobs –
continue to use – the rush hour tubes
Glassy stare – away from mounds –
but pleasant in crush – and bounce around.

"And now the last one Madam!"

If upon your lawn is seen –
a gift from heaven – all dressed in green
Don't hesitate – the choice is yours –
drag her in – and lock the doors.

If secretary – with your cup of tea –
is prepared to sit – on your bended knee
Don't spill the tea – make trousers damp –
next ten minutes – have awful cramp.

Break-down

Motoring home – in evening rush.
Engine stops – a deathly hush.
Don't go berserk – at lead and tear it.
Show your charm – just grin and bear it.

Ode to the Phone Bill

Whilst at home – and all alone –
Birthday greetings – on the phone –
From Australia – I'm glad she rang –
But reverse charges? – I'll see her hang.

British food ships under Naval and aerial escort

Pensioner in the Pub

Of days of yore – he is a bore – and speaks of many climes –
of ships and seas – and coconut trees – and thinks they were hard times.
His ships all rolled their guts out – seas cleared the fo'cstle deck –
to hear the way he tells it – each ship became a wreck.

Of wooden ships and iron men – of mornings scrubbing decks –
sand and canvas – holy stones – Petty Officers on your necks.
Coils of hose – sea water that froze – in scuppers and on beading –
bare foot dabtoe – a boy in the Fleet –"Where is all this leading?"

You'll hear him talk of Honolulu – to Waikiki on a bathroom grating –
this of course – the sort of thing – that he did as a rating.
Then maybe he'll talk about – the years he did at sea –
but, was that crossing the harbour – where the ferry used to be?

"Stream the fog buoy" – "Out PV's" – "Prepare to tow ship aft" –
"Man the sea boat" – "Pick up dan buoy" – so much he felt quite daft.
Hoped that he could bare up – tot helped to end of day –
mind and muscle – in evolutions – has he earned his pay?

Main derrick – hoisting picket-boat – and launches One and Two –
you cannot dodge this harbour chore – you find that they need you.
"Man the guys – hoist away" – till tackle is 'two blocks' –
"Lower away – easy does it" – "Secure her on her chocks".

Fleet manouvres – exercises – away in starboard lifeboat –
fire torpedoes – pick them up – hope that they all float.
Snap on clip hook – pass on second line – right down to the tail –
heavy haul – on the tail-line – recovery – never fail.

Gunnery, guns and gunsights – ammunition stack on stack –
"Load and fire" – "Sight a bit higher" – "Stand clear the recoil, Jack".
Then it's "Quarters clean guns" – "Sponge out" and "Pull through" –
polish and rags – from cleaning bags – the guns must look brand new.

Mooring swivel – Blake screw stopper – on fo'cstle part of ship –
steel wire hawser – needs eye-splice quickly – use a bulldog grip.
Heave in cable – stow the anchors – prepare the ship for sea –
lash the cables – shipping it fo'ard – "Why is it always me?"

Forenoon watch – work on deck – close up for his 'trick' –
"Hands to Dinner" – greasy hot pot – stave off feeling sick.
Quick caulk down – on wooden mess-stool – and dream of coral sands –
"Rise and shine – you've had your time" – "Both Watches of the Hands".

"Switch to LA …GREEN SHIP!"
(Afterthought: Or shall I take more water with it?)

Now's his chance – get in the chains – show how to 'heave the lead'–
but not too careful how it's done – stops it landing on his head.
Frozen hands – cold as charity – bound to get it right soon –
cause Skipper apoplexy – "Don't know the words – only know the tune".

A cables length – sweep ahead – ships all stretched in line –
Skipper orders "Hard a starboard" – "Why is it always tot-time?"
Matelots precious liquor – on tables, stools and deck –
curses, oaths and insults – "Like to wring his f..f..laming neck".

He's held his ground – he's paid one round – and now it's nearly three.
You lot – back to work quite sharp – while he goes home to tea.
Rest assured – his big reward – these yarns – they're all quite true –
and listen – while we're at it – I'll have a pint from you....

Naval Terms Illustrated – "Give way together"

"… spitfire! Spitfire!! SPITFIRE!!!"

Naval Terms Illustrated – "Draught"

Ode to the Ancient Mariner

Cradle snatcher – once supreme –
In flat round hat and bell-bots preen.
'Pulling' birds – once automatic –
Can now only 'pull' – a geriatric.

Ode to the Dancing Master

Twinkle toes in days of yore
Can hardly crawl now to the door.
Disco dancing – not his scene
Prefers to sup his Ovaltine.

Misty Memories

See him in the public bar –
sipping bitter from his 'jar'.
Wars are won – some battles lost –
millions of lives – at frightful cost.

He has done his little bit –
on land, the air or on a ship.
When duty called – he wasn't lacking –
he's one you can't accuse of slacking.

Can you read behind his eyes?
The turquoise sea, those tropic skies.
Travels to those lands so far –
brown job, fly boy, or jolly tar?

Lazy, carefree, tropic days –
burning sun and thick heat haze.
Not quite so nice – with athletes' feet –
carbuncles, desert sores and prickly heat.

Statistics prove his luck was in –
no burial service, hammock or box for him.
He returns – and settles down –
to steady job – in own hometown.

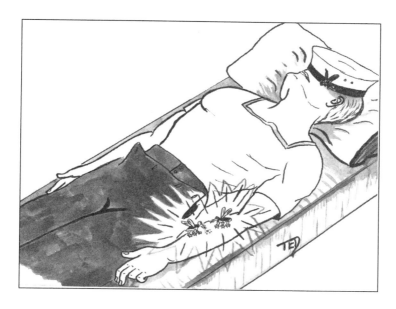

"Canned sailor again – when do we get some fresh meat?"

Shortly then he finds a girl –
of twinkling eye and dancing curl.
Woos her, wins her, finds a house –
for him – his love – his brand new spouse.

Then offsprings soon appear –
"Another one? So soon – my dear?"
See them grow – and off to school –
"With four – like that – he is a fool".

From school to work – they knuckle down –
and thought their Dad was quite a clown.
His itchy feet no longer strayed –
he raised the kids – was well behaved.

Exams at 'O' and 'A' they need –
he's done it too – they should take heed.
To help them all – he did his best –
very soon – they flew the nest.

They travelled far – they live abroad.
Kids gone – no wife – Dad's getting bored.
Chasing blondes – he thinks a farce –
his 'legs' have gone on him at last.

Sitting quietly drinking beer –
dreaming of his yesteryear.
Now his morale is touching zero –
yesterday's forgotten hero.

Glossary

1 cwt (one hundredweight) – approximately 50 kgs

150 yards – approximately 137 metres

20 lbs – 9 kgs

250 lbs – approximately 113 kgs in new money

3Rs – reading, writing and arithmetic

Ack-Ack Class – ship fitted with anti-aircraft guns

'Altmark' incident – 16th February 1940, when a British destroyer rescued British prisoners from a German supply ship 'the Altmark' in Norwegian waters, with cries of 'The Navy's here'

the Andrew – slang name for the Royal Navy

ASA – Amateur Swimming Association

Backward – refers to boys / men who fall below the standard of the rest of the class; tending to become a hindrance to the remainder and placed in the 'backward' PT class

Banyans – loose flannel jacket and / or shirt

Baths – swimming pool

'Bear' – *see Crossing the Line*

Bells (and round hat) / bell bots – bell bottomed trousers and cap, part of No.1 uniform for an ordinary rating

the Bloke – nickname of Commander rank for Shore Establishment or large warship

Bootnecks – Royal Marines

Buff (2nd class) – a junior stoker

Capt 'D' – senior captain of a destroyer squadron

Chats – refers to Naval port and RM base of Chatham

Chats and Guzz lads – *see individual references to locations*

ChERA – chief engine room artificer

Clubswinger – All servicemen and ex-servicemen are aware that Physical Training Instructors in the Services are of probable doubtful parentage. Those in the Royal Navy are the same, but are surrounded by salt water and are known as 'Clubs' short for 'clubswinger' because of the badge of crossed Indian clubs worn as a badge of office on their singlets

Crossing the Line – unofficial but traditional fun ceremony performed when a warship crosses the Equator. King Neptune and his Court initiate novices into the Brotherhood of the Sea. There is no differentiation of treatment between men and officers during the lathering, mock shaving and throwing to the Bears, backwards into a full tank of water

Cruising Station Watch – the basic art of getting from A to B

Crusher – ship's police

Dabtoe – (able-bodied) seaman rating

Dan buoy – small buoy used to mark mine swept area

Dghajsa – a typical Maltese fisherman's boat

Dhobey – washing clothes, adopted from a Hindi word

Dog watch / 'dogs' – two short two-hour periods placed in the 24-hour Naval shift pattern

DPTS – Directorate of Naval Physical Training and Sport, Portsmouth

DQs – detention quarters

Duck's disease – shortness of legs bringing bottom closer to the ground

Duck suits – white tropical uniform

Duck suit top – probably refers to ratings' square collared tops

E boat alley – German mine laying boats in eastern British coastal waters

ERA – engine room artificer

Fanny – vessel used for the collection of the mess deck's rum issue

Five-eighths nut and bolt bender – imperial version of an engineer

FOM – Flag Officer, Malta

Futtock rigging – futtocks are the short rope ladders between the ratlines and the top timbers (platform) of a ship's wooden mast

GC badge – Good Conduct badge

Ganges – a river in India, but also a previous on-shore Naval Establishment in Suffolk, HMS Ganges

Guzz – nickname for the Naval base at Devonport in Plymouth

Half-leader (1/2 leader) – the ship carrying the Commanding Officer second in charge to the Captain 'D'

Hammock ladder – very much like a sky hook

Hawsers – thick steel cable for mooring (or towing) a ship

HET – higher education test

Jack – Royal Navy sailor

Jankers – punishment

Jossman – Master-at-Arms

Killick – Leading Hand, the first rung on RN promotion ladder

Layer – Senior member of Naval gun's crew

'Lodge and comp' – lodge and compensation for living 'out' i.e. ration allowance

Marlin spikes – metal spikes for separating rope or wire

Matelot – Royal Navy sailor

Muscle Mansion – refers to the Royal Navy School of Physical Training, previously at Pitt Street, Portsmouth

Naval Patrol – Shore patrol (Naval police)

No. 1 – 1st Lieutenant

No. 1s – best bib and tucker dress uniform

No-badge Killick – Leading Hand without any GC badge

Nozzers – new entry trainee seamen

OD – ordinary deckhand

OOW – Officer of the Watch

Oscar (the model) – a medical model of a human

'Part of Ship' – a sailor's place of work

'Pate' – slang for slaphead

Patrol (Naval) – Shore patrol

Paying Off pendant – a long flag flown from the mast on sailing from the last port at the end of a ship's commission

Piping of the Still – piping the Ship's Company to attention

Pitt Street (baths) – RN School of Physical Training

PO – Petty Officer

Pompey – nickname for Portsmouth

PQ 18 – convoy identification, to Murmansk 1942

PT – physical training

PTI – Physical Training Instructor

A Pusser – any Officer of the Supply and Secretariat specialisation

The Pusser – Supply Officer

PV's – paravane, a device used to cut moorings of submerged mines

Quals – newly qualified PT instructors

Raff types – members of the Royal Air Force

Ratlines – ladders made of rope, connecting to wooden masts

RE – Rosyth Establishment

Red Caps – military police

RHA – Royal Horse Artillery

RM – Royal Marine

RN – Royal Navy

RNH – Royal Naval Hospital

RSM – Regimental Sergeant Major

Sentry – guard

Shellback – a sailor who has been at sea so long that limpet shells and barnacles are encrusting his back

'Skate' – work shy person

Skylark – (verb), messing about, mucking around. (refer to PT Office, Standing Orders 1953 Section V no.76 'Swimming Bath / Bath surrounds', "There is to be NO SKYLARKING or RUNNING on the Bath surrounds")

Sprog – a novice

Strop out – hanging washing on any made-up line of rope

Tar (jolly) – sailor

Temeraire – on-shore naval PT Training Establishment, HMS Temeraire

Tin gear – aluminium buckets, pots and pans and so on

Tot – half gill measure of rum

Traps – trapeze

Truck to keel – top to bottom, as 'truck' is the circular wooden cap to a mast

'Up Spirits' – piped order initiating collection and issue of daily tot

Valletta 'Gut' – Malta's old red light district

Victory 1 – a building / barracks at the naval base in Portsmouth used as a depot for several ships

White Caps – more military police

Wood butcher – ship's carpenter

WRNS / Wrens – Women's Royal Naval Service

About Help for Heroes

Help for Heroes (H4H) was launched in October 2007 out of a desire to help the wounded members of the Armed Forces coming back from Afghanistan and Iraq. H4H believes that anyone who volunteers to serve in time of war, knowing that they may risk all, is a hero. Help for Heroes is very simple; strictly non political, they accept that wars happen under any government and are not critical; they simply want to help.

To date H4H has raised over £23 million to support our service personnel. They have allocated the first £8 million to the task of helping to provide the new swimming pool and gym complex at DMRC Headley Court. Grants have also been made to Troop Aid, Battle Back, SSAFA and Combat Stress.

H4H's latest venture will be helping to fund the Pathfinder project for an Army Convalescent Centre in Edinburgh. H4H, working with the Army and Service Charity Erskine, will be creating a house for 12 Solders to live while they begin to launch back into their lives after sustaining injuries. The intention is that once the concept has been proven successful, there will be up to 7 other such houses established, with H4H's funding, around the country.

For each copy sold, a donation will be made to the Help for Heroes charity.